NANOCLAYS
Synthesis, Characterization and Applications

The Author

Dr. Hasmukh A. Patel received his Ph.D. from the Central Salt and Marine Chemical Research Institute (CSMCRI), Gujarat, India under the supervision of Dr. Raksh Vir Jasra and Dr. Hari C. Bajaj. He is a life time member of Materials Research Society of India. He is awarded Gold Medal for securing first position at Master degree level in Materials Science from Sardar Patel University. He has been working in the multidisciplinary research field which includes layered materials, organic-organic hybrids, polymer nanocomposites, drug delivery carriers, catalysis, adsorption and porous materials for gas separations. He visited Politecnico di Torino, Italy as a researcher from 2009-2010 and presently working at Korea Advanced Institute of Science and Technology (KAIST), South Korea. He published more than 25 international publications, delivered more than 20 presentations and published 6 Korean patents.

NANOCLAYS
Synthesis, Characterization and Applications

Dr. Hasmukh A. Patel

2014
Scholars World
A Division of
Astral International Pvt. Ltd.
New Delhi – 110 002

Published by   : **Scholars World**
                     A Division of
                     Astral International Pvt. Ltd.
                     – ISO 9001:2008 Certified Company –
                     4760-61/23, Ansari Road, Darya Ganj
                     New Delhi-110 002
                     Ph. 011-43549197, 23278134
                     E-mail: info@astralint.com
                     Website: www.astralint.com

Laser Typesetting : **SSMG Computer Graphics**
                      Delhi - 110 084

Printed at   : **Replika Press Pvt. Ltd.**

PRINTED IN INDIA

Contents

Chapter 1
Introduction

1.1. Clay Minerals

The term *clay* has a different connotations and, therefore, should be defined when it is used. Clay is used both as a rock term and as a particle size term. As a rock term, clay is used for a natural, earthy, fine-grained material composed largely of a limited group of crystalline minerals known as the clay minerals. As a particle size term, clay is used for the category that includes the smallest particles. Soil investigators and mineralogists generally use 2 μm as the maximum size, although the Wentworth scale [1] defines clay as a material finer than 4 μm. Grim [2] used the term clay material for any fine-grained, natural, earthy, argillaceous material; in this way, the term can include clays, shales, or argillites, and some soils if these are argillaceous. Clay is an abundantly available raw material and has an amazing variety of uses and properties that depend on clay mineral component, nonclay mineral composition, presence of organic material, the type and amount of exchangeable ions and soluble salts and clay's texture.

Clays are comprised of certain groups of hydrous aluminum, magnesium, and iron silicates that may contain sodium, calcium, potassium and other ions. These silicates are called the clay minerals, and their classifications are shown in Figure 1.1. The specific clay minerals are

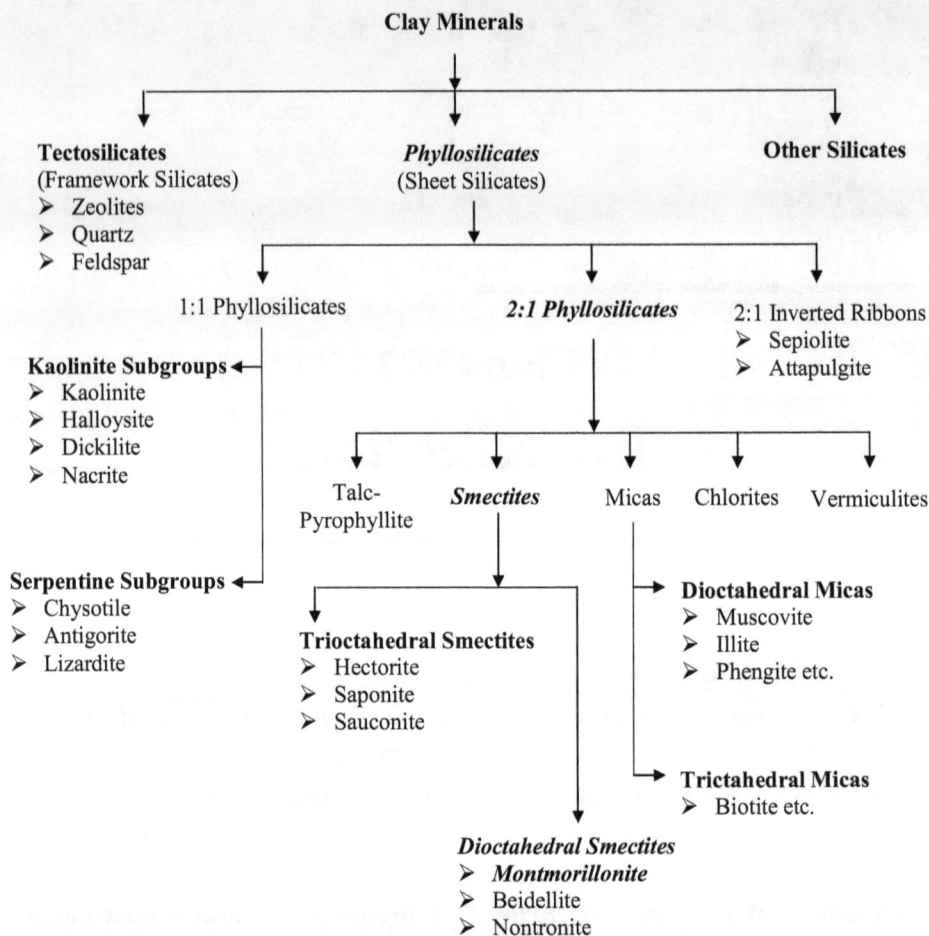

Figure 1.1. Classification of clay minerals.

identified by several techniques, including X-ray diffraction [3], differential thermal analysis [4], electron microscopy [5] and infrared spectrometry [6]. Identification and quantification of the clay minerals and nonclay minerals present in a clay material is important because its uses and engineering properties are controlled largely by these two factors.

1.1.1. Geology and Occurrence of Smectite

Smectite is the name for a group of sodium, calcium, magnesium, iron and lithium containing aluminum silicates, which includes the individual minerals such as sodium montmorillonite, calcium montmorillonite, nontronite, saponite, and hectorite. The rock in which these smectite minerals are usually dominant is **Bentonite**. The name bentonite was first suggested in 1898 by Knight [7] and is the term commonly used to describe the industrial mineral. The term bentonite was defined by Ross and Shannon [8], it was restricted to a clay material altered from a glassy igneous material, usually a tuff or volcanic ash. Wright [9] suggested that bentonite was any clay composed dominantly of a smectite clay mineral and whose physical properties are dictated by this clay mineral. Grim and Guven [10] used Wright's definition in their book on bentonites because there are many clays designated as bentonite that did not originate by the alteration of volcanic ash or tuff. Therefore, the term bentonite usually is not based on the mode of origin.

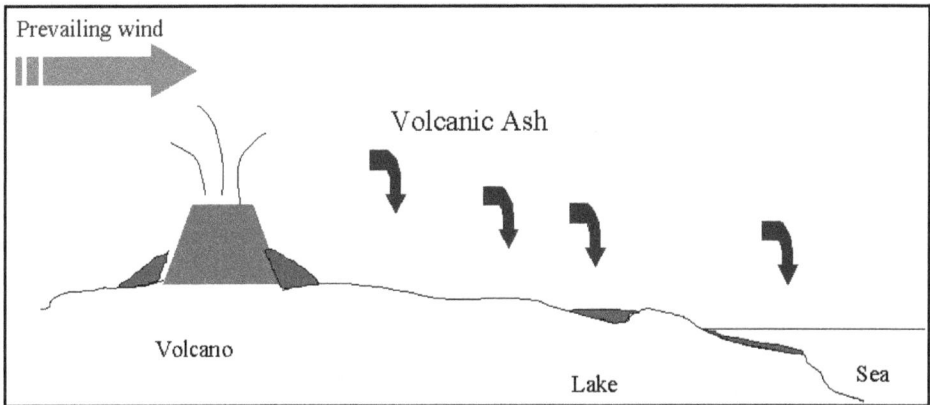

Figure 1.2. Formation of bentonite during the Cretaceous period (85–125 million years ago).

Bentonites in which sodium montmorillonites is the major mineral constituent commonly have a high swelling capacity [11]. The largest and best quality sodium bentonite deposits known in the world are located in South Dakota, Wyoming, and Montana [12]. These clays are commonly called Western or Wyoming bentonites. Huge amounts of bentonite deposits are available throughout the western and southern regions of India, particularly Gujarat and Rajasthan. The bentonite is generally light yellowish green on the outcrop, becoming bluish green away from the outcrop. The highest quality swelling clay is the yellowish green bentonite, which has been weathered and oxidized. The major nonclay minerals present in the clay spur bentonite bed are quartz, opal-CT, feldspar, mica, and some zeolites. Locally calcite and gypsum may also be present.

1.1.2. Composition and structure of Smectites

The clays used in the formation of nanoclays belong to smectite group clays, the most common of which are montmorillonite (MMT) and hectorite, where octahedral site is isomorphically substituted. Other smectite group clays are beidellite (BDT), nontronite (NT), volkonskoite, saponite and sauconite, in which tetrahedral site is isomorphically substituted as shown in Table 1.1.

Table 1.1. Members of dioctahedral and trioctahedral smectites [11].

Smectite Family		Ionic Formla
Dioctahedral	**Montmorillonite**	$Si_4 (Al_{2-x}Mg_x) O_{10} (OH)_2 (*M_x \cdot nH_2O)$
	Beidellite	$(Si_{4-x}Al_x) Al_2 O_{10} (OH)_2 (M_x \cdot nH_2O)$
	Nontronite	$(Si_{4-x}Al_x) Fe_2 O_{10} (OH)_2 (M_x \cdot nH_2O)$
	Volkonskoite	$(Si_{4-x}Al_x) Cr_2 O_{10} (OH)_2 (M_x \cdot nH_2O)$
Trioctahedral	**Hectorite**	$Si_4 (Mg_{3-y} Li_y) O_{10} (OH)_2 (*M_y \cdot nH_2O)$
	Saponite	$(Si_{4-y}Al_y) Mg_3 O_{10} (OH)_2 (M_y \cdot nH_2O)$
	Sauconite	$(Si_{4-y}Al_y) Zn_3 O_{10} (OH)_2 (M_y \cdot nH_2O)$

*M_x and M_y are exchangeable cations like Na^+, K^+, Li^+ and Ca^{+2}.

A unit layer of smectite minerals (Tetrahedral-Octahedra-Tetrahedral, TOT) is formed by the bonding through oxygen bridges of one alumina sheet composed of octahedrons [O: $AlO_3 (OH)_3$] between two silica sheets composed of tetrahedrons [T: SiO_4]. These three-layer units are stacked one above another with oxygens in neighboring layers adjacent to each other, with thickness of 1 nm, as shown in Figure 3. The bentonite powder consists of the agglomeration of thousands of TOT layers. It produces a weak bond, allowing water and other polar molecules to enter between layers and induce an expansion of the mineral structure [13].

The lateral dimensions of these layers vary from 200 nm to several microns depending on the particular silicate. Stacking of the layers leads to a regular van der Walls gap between them called the *interlayer* or *gallery*. Although the basal spacing is 1.2-1.3 nm at ambient condition, it can be varied with respect to amount of hydrophilic or organophilic groups situated at gallery. Isomorphic substitution within the layer (either in octahedral or tetrahedral site) by Mg^{2+}, Fe^{2+} or Al^{3+} generates negative charges that are normally counter balanced by hydrated alkali or alkaline

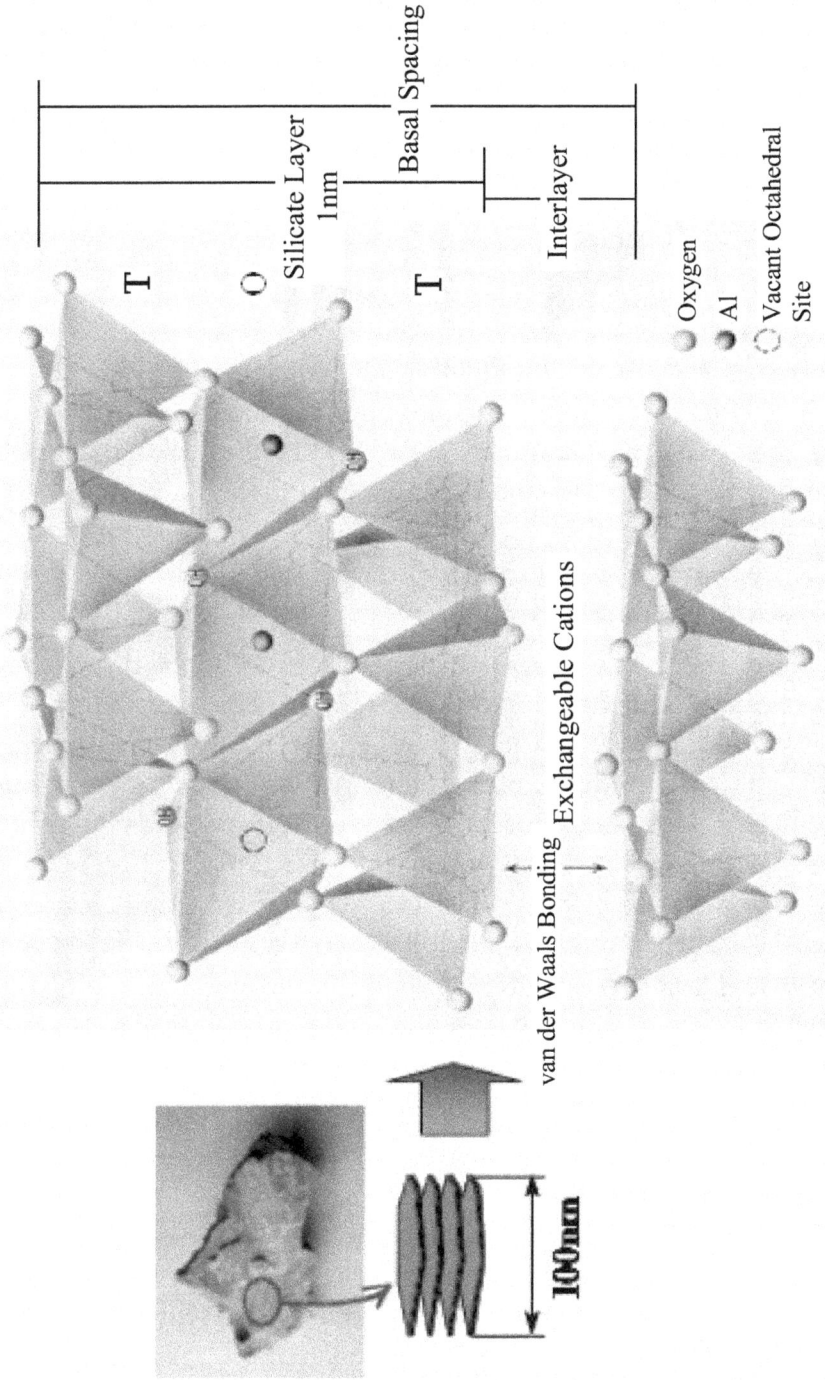

Figure 1.3. The structure of 2:1 layered silicates.

earth cations (Na^+, K^+, Ca^+, Li^+ etc.) residing in the interlayer. Because of the relatively weak forces between the layers, intercalation of various molecules, an even polymer, between the layers is facile [14].

1.1.3. Purification of Bentonites

With the possible exception of vermiculites and micas, clay minerals are found mixed or associated with other minerals and/or amorphous materials. Identification of bentonites in a raw clay or soil always requires a purification step. This is because the presence of carbonates, iron oxides or organic materials interferes with the identification procedure [15]. Carbonates must be decomposed, especially when the purified clay is to be used in colloid studies as the calcium and magnesium ions in carbonates impede the complete delamination of the MMT. Carbonates can be decomposed by the addition of dilute hydrochloric acid, taking care that the pH does not drop below 4.5 to avoid any attack on structure of MMT. After the decomposition of carbonates the sample should be washed to remove the dissolved cations.

Similarly, the presence of hydroxides prevents optimal dispersion of MMT and successful fractionation. Iron hydroxides are removed by complexing the multivalent cations with citrate. Firstly, Fe (III) must be reduced with sodium dithionite to Fe (II) which forms a stable citrate complex. The treated samples are washed with de-ionized water to remove complexing cations [16]. Likewise, organic materials must be removed because high amounts of humic materials associated with the bentonite, can render X-ray identification difficult. Organic materials, even in small amounts, can also exert a strong influence on the mechanical properties and flow behavior of MMT dispersions. The organic materials can be oxidized with hydrogen peroxide.

The structure of MMT is affected by above chemical treatments which are used for removal of carbonates, hydroxides and organics. However, complete enrichment of bentonite may only be achieved at a laboratory scale rather than at an industrial scale. Even then, no more than 90 per cent enrichment is usually achievable [11]. The classical gentle purification method consists of replacing the exchangeable cations with Na^+ followed by washing with distilled water and sedimentation. Washing removes excess salts as described before and also enables fine impurities to be separated. The sedimentation technique based on Stoke's Law is simple and cost effective [12];

$$r^2 = \frac{9\,\eta h}{2(d1-d2)\,g\,t}$$

where,

r: Radius of given particle (assuming spherical, μ),

h: Height (cm) through which it falls in time "t" in minutes,

g: Acceleration due to gravity,

d1 and d2: Densities of solid and liquid respectively and

η: Viscosity of water.

1.1.4. Montmorillonite (MMT) – Water Interaction

It is well known that when MMT is dispersed in distilled water, positively charged edges are attracted to negatively charged surfaces of the platelets to form a three dimensional "house of cards" structure which contains hundreds or thousands of silicate platelets [17]. The formation of "house of cards" structure in smectite clay dispersion can be explained in relation to double layer theory. According to this model, most of the exchangeable ions in the clay dispersion tend to accumulate, due to electrostatic attraction, near the negative faces of the platelets, but simultaneously have a tendency to diffuse away from platelet surfaces toward the bulk of the water where their concentration is low [18]. The equilibration of these opposing effects causes the formation of a diffuse atmosphere of counter ions, with concentration diminishing with distance from the platelet face. A negative "double layer" is thus established, consisting of the negative surface charge plus the diffuse counterions.

The analogous positive double layer is established in association with platelet edges. When an electrolyte or polar solvent is added to the dispersion, the double layers are compressed. This allows the platelet edges and faces to come more closely, resulting in a more rigid structure and consequently higher viscosity, called the formation of "house of cards" structure. If the double layers become sufficiently compressed, face-face van der Waals attraction will predominate and the house of cards colloidal structure will be lost, which results in to dispersion of 1 nm thick silicates platelets through out the matrix medium [19].

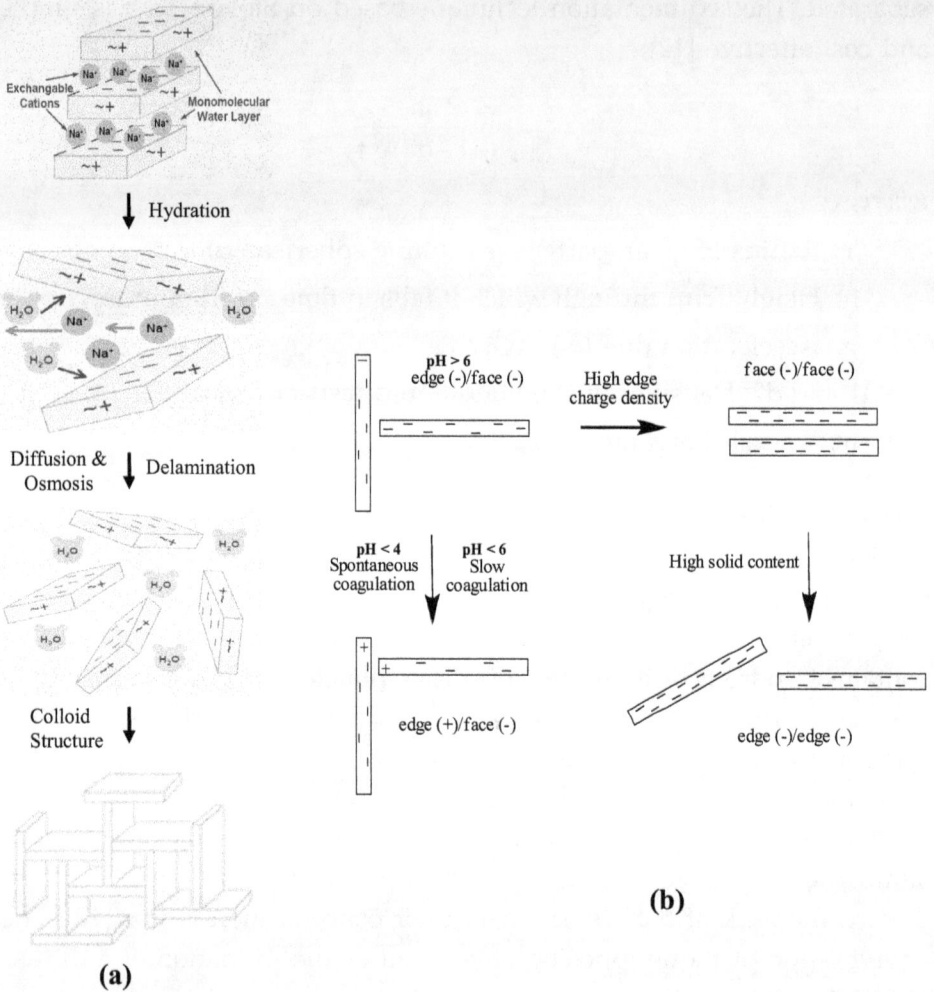

Figure 1.4. Formation of (a) "House of Cards" colloidal structure and (b) different modes of coagulation of MMT layers.

1.1.5. Nanoclays

The clays used for the preparation of nanoclays or organoclays belong to smectite group clays, the most common of which is MMT. One important consequence of the charged nature of the clays is that they are generally highly hydrophilic species and therefore naturally incompatible with a wide range of non-polar systems.

Organophilic clay (nanoclay) can be obtained by simply the ion-exchange reaction of hydrophilic clay with an organic cation such as an alkyl/aryl ammonium, phosphonium or imidazolium cations in aqueous solution or in the solid state [20-21]. The inorganic ions are exchanged with more voluminous organic onium cations. When the solubility of quaternary salts is low, water-alcohol mixtures are often used as a solvent. The ion exchange reaction has two consequences; first, the gap between the single sheets is widened, enabling organic cations chain to move in between them and second, the surface properties of each single sheet are changed from being hydrophilic to hydrophobic or organophilic as shown in Figure 1.5.

The arrangement of the intercalated surfactant cations depends on the layer charge and alkyl chain length as shown in Figure 1.6 [22]. Short chain alkylammonium ions are arranged in monolayers, longer chain alkylammonium ions in bilayers with the alkyl chain axes parallel to the silicate layers. The monolayer has a basal spacing of ~1.4 nm and the bilayer of ~1.8 nm. The monolayer rearranges in to the bilayer when the area of the flat-lying alkylammonium ions becomes larger than the equivalent area. The monolayer/bilayer transition is used to measure the charge distribution and the mean layer charge. Three layer structures of kinked alkyl chains are observed with highly charged MMT and/or long surfactants cations. This trimolecular arrangement exhibits a basal spacing of ~2.2 nm. The term pseudo is used because the positive surfactant groups are attached on the silicate layers whereas the alkyl chains assume a trimolecular arrangement by formation of kinks. Paraffin-type arrangements in the interlayer space of MMT are formed by quaternary alkylammonium ions with two or more long alkyl chains [23]. The orientation and mobility of intercalated alkylammonium ions are examined by X-ray diffraction, infrared and nuclear magnetic resonance spectroscopy [24-25].

1.1.6. Characterization Techniques for Nanoclays

There is no single or simple procedure for the characterization of bentonite. Clays and their modified organic derivatives are characterized using conventional as well as modern characterization tools which include determination of chemical compositions by gravimetric analysis, inductively coupled plasma (ICP-AES) or XRF, cation exchange capacity (CEC) using standard ammonium acetate method, surface area measurement, Fourier transform infrared spectroscopy (FT-IR), powdered X-ray diffraction

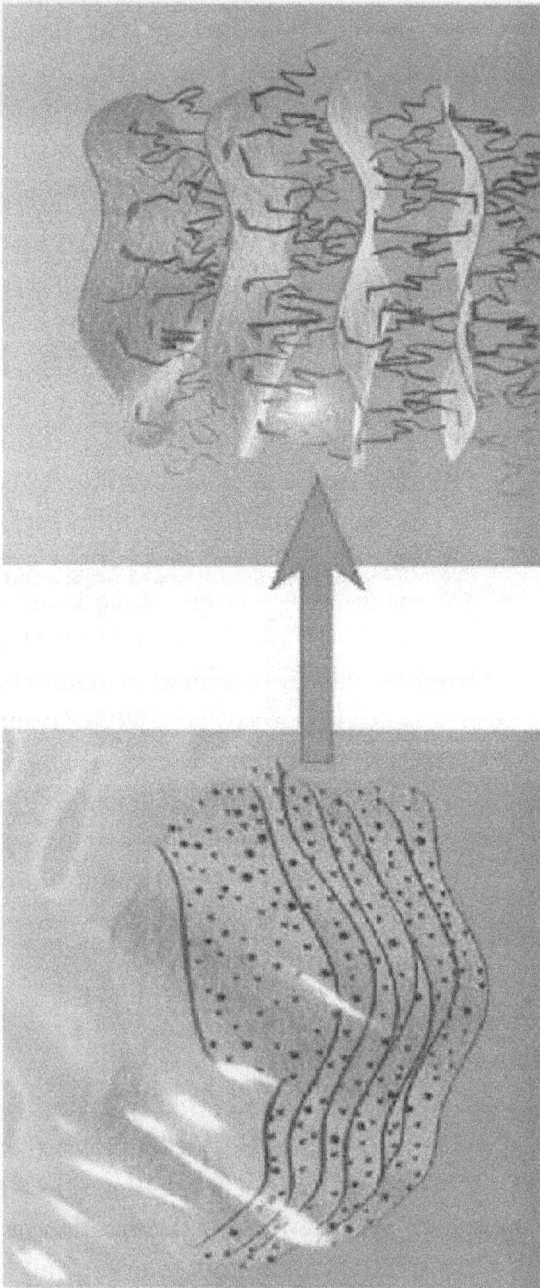

Figure 1.5. Schematic picture of an ion-exchange reaction.

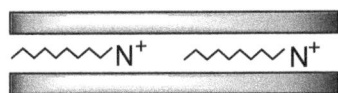

Monolayers

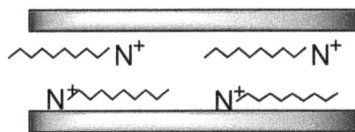

Bilayers

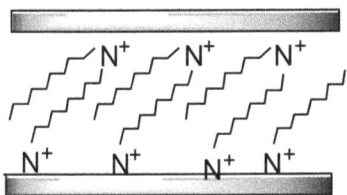

Pseudo-trimolecular layers

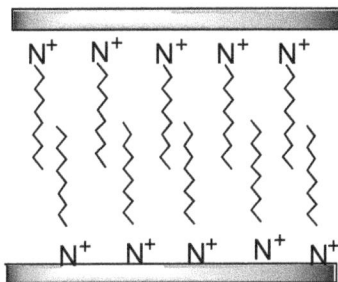

Paraffin-type arragements

Figure 1.6. Arrangements of alkylammonium ions in the interlayer space of MMT.

(PXRD) and others. Generally, ionic formula is computed on the basis of its chemical compositions, charge density and cation exchange capacity of clays which provide information about the types of layered silicates. The instrumental techniques mainly, FT-IR and PXRD are basic methods for identification of clay structure.

The FTIR spectrum for montmorillonite recorded as KBr pellet and its band assignments are shown in Figure 1.7. The broad band centered near 3400 cm^{-1} is due to -OH stretching band for interlayer water. The bands at 3620 and 3698 cm^{-1} are due to -OH band stretch for Al-OH and Si-OH. The shoulders and broadness of the structural -OH band are mainly due to contributions of several structural -OH groups present in the clay. However, the position of the band maximum is clearly indicative of the chemical composition of montmorillonite. The overlaid absorption peaks in the region of 1640 cm^{-1} in the FTIR spectrum of purified clay (MMT) is attributed to -OH bending mode in water (adsorbed water). The characteristic peak at 1115 cm^{-1} is due to Si–O stretching (out-of-plane) for montmorillonite. The peak at 1035 cm^{-1} is attributed to Si-O stretching (in-plane) vibration for layered silicates. The IR peaks at 915, 875 and 836 cm^{-1} are attributed to AlAlOH, AlFeOH and AlMgOH bending vibrations, respectively.

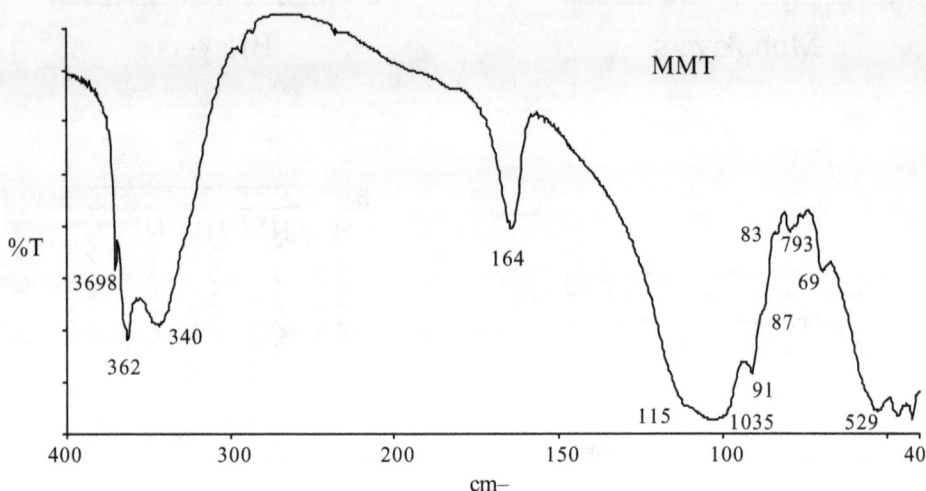

Figure 1.7. FTIR spectra of MMT recorded as KBr pellet.

Table 1.2. Band assignments for montmorillonite (MMT).

Maxima, cm^{-1}	Assignments	Maxima, cm^{-1}	Assignments	Maxima, cm^{-1}	Assignments
3698	–OH stretching	1151	Si-O stretching, out-of-plane	836	AlMgOH bending
3620	–OH stretching	1035	Si-O stretching, in-plane	793	Platy form of tridymite
3400	–OH stretching, Hydration	915	AlAlOH bending	692	Quartz
1640	–OH bending, Hydration	875	AlFeOH bending	529	Si-O bending

PXRD is the basic technique for clay mineral analysis. After preliminary removal of sand, clay is separated from silt by centrifugation or sedimentation from suspensions. PXRD patterns are obtained and compared with standards for identification of minerals. Comparisons are complicated, however, by variations in diffraction patterns arising from differences in amounts of absorbed water, by the presence of imperfections in the crystal lattice structure of the minerals, and by mixed-layer structures formed by interstratifications of minerals within a single particle.

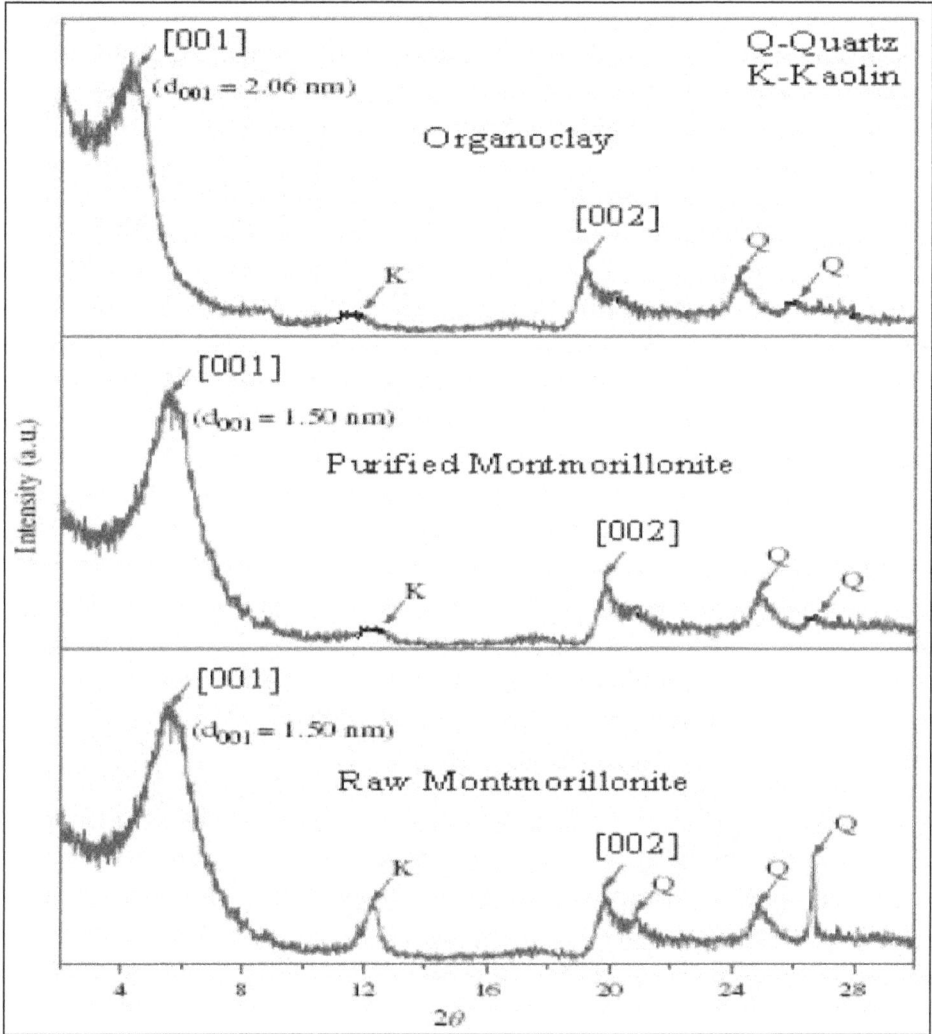

Figure 1.8. PXRD patterns of raw, purified and organically modified montmorillonite.

PXRD is one of the most important techniques to determine the structural geometry, texture and also to illustrate impurities (kaolin, quartz, calcite, etc) in layered silicates which are present in clays. Generally, the PXRD pattern (Figure 1.8) indicates that there is presence of impurities such as kaolin (K) and quartz (Q) in raw MMT which are partly or fully removed on further purification by sedimentation. The reflections relative to the planes [001] and [002] confirmed the presence of montmorillonite as main phase. The PXRD pattern of the organoclay revealed a shift in the position of [001] planes (2θ changed from 5.7 to 4.32 degree), meaning an increase in the basal spacing of this plane. The increase was relatively large, from 1.5 – 2.1 nm and confirms the occurrence of organic molecule intercalation between silicate platelets. From the PXRD of organoclays (Figure 1.8), it is also observed that the peaks from [002] planes of montmorillonite, were not affected during this treatment. This observation highlights that the unique effect of organic modifier in layered silicates structure is the intercalation of [001] planes of montmorillonite. The basal spacing of layered silicates depends on the kind of organic modifier, with bulkier organic modifier as well as its high concentration resulting into higher interlayer spacing.

1.2. Polymer Nanocomposites

The mystery of the 'nano-world' has been progressively exposed in recently years. The nanometer scale is simply a range of 1-100 nm. The real interest in nanotechnology is to create revolutionary properties and functions by tailoring materials and designing devices on the nanometer scale. The fillers used in polymer nanocomposites are of one, two or three nano-dimensional. The dimensionality of fillers is illustrated in Figure 1.9. Polymer/layered silicates nanocomposites have a one nano-dimension, *i.e.*, the thickness of the layer (1 nm in case of MMT) with lateral dimension of more than 100 nm.

Polymer/layered silicates nanocomposites (PLSN) are a new class of composites. The filler is present in the form of sheets of one to a few nanometer thick and hundreds to thousands nanometers long, and their study in different polymer matrices will constitute the main object of this contribution. PLSN have been more widely investigated probably because the starting clay materials are easily available, filler loading required are 3-6 per cent w/w and because their intercalation and exfoliation chemistry has been studied for a long time [26-33].

Compared to conventional polymer composites and the pristine polymer matrix, PLSN can exhibit many advantages, including [34-38].

☆ They are lighter in weight than conventionally filled polymers because high degree of stiffness and strength are realized with far less high density inorganic material.

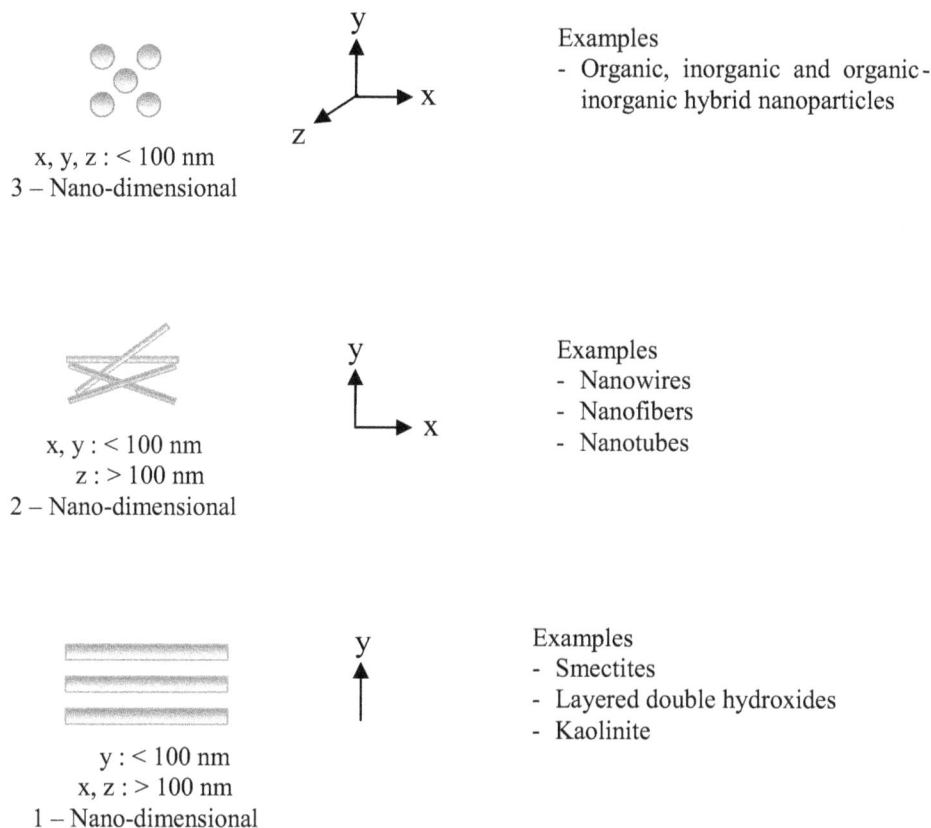

x, y, z : < 100 nm
3 – Nano-dimensional

Examples
- Organic, inorganic and organic-inorganic hybrid nanoparticles

x, y : < 100 nm
z : > 100 nm
2 – Nano-dimensional

Examples
- Nanowires
- Nanofibers
- Nanotubes

y : < 100 nm
x, z : > 100 nm
1 – Nano-dimensional

Examples
- Smectites
- Layered double hydroxides
- Kaolinite

Figure 1.9. Dimensionality of fillers used in polymer nanocomposites.

☆ They exhibit outstanding diffusional barrier properties without requiring a multipolymer-layered design.

☆ Their mechanical properties are potentially superior to unidirectional fiber-reinforced polymers, because reinforcement from the inorganic layers will occur in two dimensions rather than in one.

☆ Improve solvent resistance, greater dimensional stability and superior flame retardancy.

These potential properties enhancements have led to increased applications of PLSN in various fields, such as the automotive industry (exterior and interior body parts and fuel tanks), packaging industry (bottles, containers, and plastic films), electronic industry (packaging materials and exterior parts of electronic devices), coating industry (paints, wire enamel coatings, etc.) and aerospace industry (body parts of airplanes and exterior surface coatings) [39-43].

The first commercial application of these materials was the use of clay/nylon-6 nanocomposites as timing belt covers for Toyota cars, in collaboration with Ube in 1991. Shortly after this, Unitika introduced nylon-6 nanocomposites for engine covers on Mitsubishi's GDI engines [44]. In August 2001, General Motors and Basell announced the application of clay/polyolefin nanocomposites as a step assistant component for GMC Safari and Chevrolet Astro vans. This was followed by the application of these nanocomposites in the doors of Chevrolet Impalas [45]. More recently, Noble Polymers has developed clay/polypropylene nanocomposites for structural seat backs in the Honda Acura [46], while Ube is developing clay/nylon-12 nanocomposites for automotive fuel lines and fuel system components. In addition to automotive applications, clay/polymer nanocomposites have been used to improve barrier resistance in beverage applications. Alcoa CSI has applied multilayer clay/polymer nanocomposites as barrier liner materials for enclosure applications [47]. Honeywell has developed commercial clay/nylon-6 nanocomposite products, Aegis TM NC resin, for drink packaging applications [48]. More recently, Mitsubishi Gas Chemical and Nanocor have co-developed Nylon-MXD6 nanocomposites for multilayered polyethyleneterephthalate (PET) bottle applications [49].

Table 1.3. Comparison of physical properties of polyamide filled different fillers.

Samples	Pristine Polymer	3-5 per cent Nanoclay	30 per cent Mineral	30 per cent Glass Fiber
Tensile strength, psi	7250	11800	8000	23000
Flexural modulus, psi	120	500	650	1000
Heat distortion temperature, C	66	110	120	194
Specific gravity	1.3	1.14	1.36	1.35

Source: RTP Co.

It is estimated that there will be 60 million pounds of polymer nanocomposites in production by 2008. The value of this market is forecast to reach about $211 million by then [50]. It is also estimated that widespread use of polymer nanocomposites by car manufacturers could save over 1.5 billion liters of gasoline annually and reduce CO_2 emissions by nearly 10 billion pounds. 15 years from now it is possible that you could own a car made completely out of advanced polymer nanocomposites.

Any physical mixture of a polymer and an inorganic material (such as clay) does not form a nanocomposite. Conventional polymer composites that are prepared by reinforcing a polymer matrix with inorganic materials like reinforcing fibers and minerals have poor interaction between the organic and the inorganic components, which leads to separation into discrete phases. Therefore, the inorganic fillers are required to be added in higher concentrations to achieve enhancements in the thermo-mechanical properties of the polymer. Table 1.3 shows a comparison of the physical properties of nanocomposites and conventional composites of polyamide.

1.2.1. Methodology

The preparative methods for PLSN are divided into three main groups according to the starting materials and processing techniques. These are solution induced intercalation, in situ polymerization and melt processing [51-55].

1.2.1.1. Solution Induced Intercalation

This is based on a solvent system in which the polymer or pre-polymer is soluble and the silicate layers are swellable in solvent. The layered silicate is first swollen in a solvent, such as water, chloroform, or toluene and then the polymer and layered silicate solutions are mixed, the polymer chains intercalate and displace the solvent within the interlayer of the silicate. Upon solvent removal, the intercalated structure remains, resulting in PLSN. This approach poses difficulties for the commercial production of nanocomposites for most engineering polymers because of the high costs of the solvents and the phase separation of the synthesized products from those solvents. There are also health and safety concerns associated with the application of this technology. However, solution induced intercalation is applicable to water soluble polymers, because of the low cost of using water as a solvent and its low health and safety risks, and can be used in the commercial production of nanocomposites.

1.2.1.2. *In situ* Polymerization Method

In this method, the layered silicate is swollen within the liquid monomer or a monomer solution so the polymer formation can occur between the intercalated sheets. Polymerization can be initiated either by heat or radiation, by the diffusion of a suitable initiator, or by an organic initiator or catalyst fixed through cation exchange inside the interlayer before the swelling step. This method is capable of producing well-exfoliated nanocomposites and has been applied to a wide range of polymer systems. The technology is suitable for raw polymer manufacturers to produce clay/polymer nanocomposites in polymer synthetic processes and is also particularly useful for thermosetting polymers.

1.2.1.3. Melt Intercalation Method

The melt processing method induces the intercalation of clays and polymers during melt. This method involves annealing, statically or under shear, a mixture of the polymer and organoclays above the softening point of the polymer. The efficiency of intercalation using this method may not be as high as that of *insitu* polymerization and often the composites produced contain a partially exfoliated layered structure. However, this method has great advantages over either *insitu* polymerization or solution induced intercalation. First, this method is environmentally benign due to the absence of organic solvents. Second, it is compatible with current industrial process, such as extrusion and injection molding. Therefore, the technology has played an important role in speeding up the progress of the commercial production of clay/polymer nanocomposites. The melt intercalation method allows the use of polymers which were previously not suitable for in situ polymerization or solution intercalation.

In addition to these three major processing methods for PLSN, other fabrication techniques have been also developed. These include solid intercalation, co-vulcanization and the sol-gel method. Some of these methods are in the early stages of development and have not yet been widely applied.

1.2.2. Types of Nanocomposites and Characterization Techniques

In general, layered silicates have layer thickness on the order of 1 nm and a very high L/D aspect ratio (10–1000). A few weight percent of layered silicates that are properly dispersed throughout the polymer matrix thus create much higher surface area for polymer/filler interaction as compared to conventional composites. Depending on the strength of interfacial interactions between the polymer matrix and layered silicate, three different types of composites are thermodynamically achievable (see Figure 1.10) [56].

In conventional composites the silicate layers are flocculated due to hydroxylated edge–edge interaction of the silicate layers. We can easily distinguish both the phase (filler and matrix) in this type of composites,

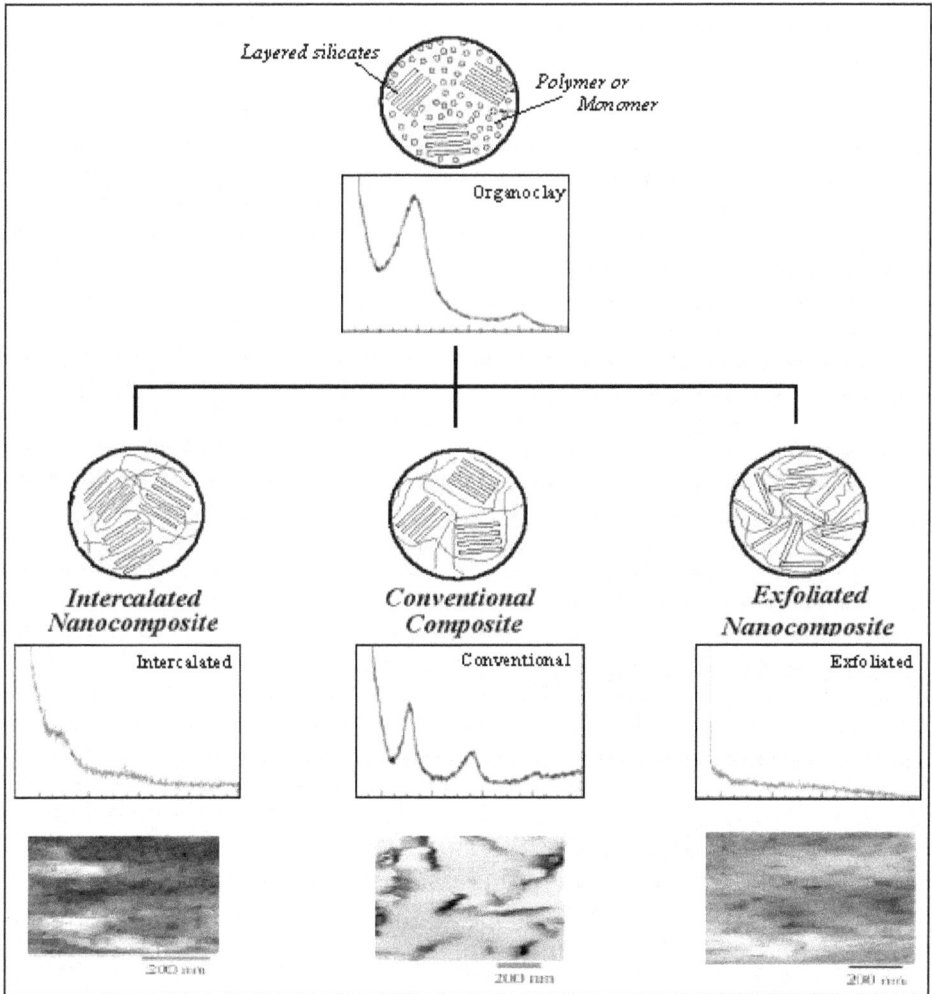

Figure 1.10. Types of polymer/layered silicate nanocomposites and TEM, XRD diffraction patterns.

also known as macro composites. Intercalated nanocomposites are resulted by insertion of a polymer into the layered silicate structure in a crystallographically regular fashion, regardless of the clay to polymer ratio. While in case of exfoliated nanocomposite, the individual clay layers are separated in a continuous polymer matrix by an average distances that depends on clay loading. Usually, the clay content of an exfoliated nanocomposite is much lower than that of an intercalated nanocomposite.

Generally, the state of dispersion and exfoliation of layered silicates has typically been established using X-ray diffraction (XRD) analysis and transmission electron micrographic (TEM) observation. Due to its easiness and availability, XRD is most commonly used to probe the structure of nanocomposite. By monitoring the position, shape, and intensity of the basal reflections (d_{001}) from the distributed silicate layers, the nanocomposite structure (intercalated or exfoliated) may be identified. For example, in an exfoliated nanocomposite, the extensive layer separation associated with the delamination of the original silicate layers in the polymer matrix results in the eventual disappearance of any coherent X-ray diffraction from the distributed silicate layers.

On the other hand, for intercalated nanocomposites, the finite layer expansion associated with the polymer intercalation results in the appearance of a new basal reflection corresponding to the larger gallery height. The XRD and TEM images are shown in Figure 1.10. Although XRD offers a convenient method to determine the interlayer spacing of the silicate layers in the original layered silicates and in the intercalated nanocomposites (within 1–4 nm), little can be said about the spatial distribution of the silicate layers or any structural non-homogeneities in nanocomposites. Additionally, some layered silicates initially do not exhibit well-defined basal reflections. Thus, peak broadening and intensity decreases are very difficult to study systematically. Therefore, conclusions concerning the mechanism of nanocomposites formation and their structure based solely on XRD patterns are only tentative. On the other hand, TEM allows a qualitative understanding of the internal structure, spatial distribution and dispersion of the layered silicates within the polymer matrix, and views of the defect structure through direct visualization. However, special care must be exercised to guarantee a representative cross section of the sample. Both TEM and XRD are essential tools for evaluating nanocomposite structure. However, TEM is time-intensive, and only gives qualitative information on the sample as a whole, while wide-angle peaks in XRD allow quantification of changes in layer spacing. Typically, when layer spacing exceed 6–7 nm in intercalated nanocomposites or when the layers become relatively disordered in exfoliated nanocomposites, associated XRD features weaken to the point of not being useful. However, recent simultaneous small angle X-ray scattering (SAXS) and XRD studies yielded quantitative characterization of nanostructure and crystallite structure in some nanocomposites [57].

1.3. Nanoclays as Rheological Modifiers in Paints

Nanoclays obtained by interaction of alkyl ammonium cations act as a thixotropic agent in paints, inks, greases and cosmetics. A small addition of nanoclays can greatly enhance the rheological properties of the paint system. These properties prevent pigment settling and sagging on vertical surfaces and gloss is minimally affected due to the low levels of addition. Rheological modifiers control the flow properties of liquid systems such as paints, inks, emulsions or pigment suspensions by increasing the medium viscosity or impart thixotropic flow behavior to liquid system. Several dispersion procedures are used for conventional organoclays; however, they all can be described by two general procedures, pre-gel addition and dry addition. Using either of these procedures, dispersion is usually carried out under shear.

The pre-gel method involves making 10-15 per cent organoclays (depending on its gel volume) dispersion in a suitable solvent using a high-speed disperser and a polar activator. Pre-gels can be made in large batches, stored and used as needed, or as the first step in the manufacturing process. Direct addition of organoclays involves adding organoclay as a dry powder prior to, or during, the grind phase in the manufacturing process. The most advantageous is after the addition of resin and solvent. This will allow the organoclay to wet out. Polar activator is then added and dispersion continued. In the wet out step, organoclay is added in the solvent under shear.

This will cause a partial deagglomeration of the platelets, but by no means complete dispersion. For complete dispersion to occur, the addition of a polar activator is necessary. The function of polar activators is to disrupt the weak van der Waal forces which tend to hold the clay platelets together. Once these platelets are separated, it allows the organic functional groups to free themselves from close association with the clay surface. These functional groups are now free to solvate in the organic liquid; *i.e.* they have a much higher affinity for the organic solvent than the inorganic clay surface (Figure 1.11).

These functional groups are part of the organic modifier that is attracted to the clay surface through electrostatic forces [58-59]. The typical structure of organoclay consists of layered silicate platelet having a long-chain organic compound bonded to its two faces. In a system containing the fully dispersed and activated organoclay additives, a gel structure is developed by edge-to-edge hydrogen bonding between hydroxyl groups on the organoclay platelet edges. Solvation of the long-chain organic molecule tails makes them stand away from the clay platelet faces. In most cases a chemical activator (also known as polar activator) is added to ensure complete delamination, dispersion, and full activation of the organoclay; however, polar activator free organically modified layered silicates had also been developed by subsequently ion exchanged organic modifier with polar functional groups. Polar activators are defined as low molecular weight compounds of a polar nature.

The most commonly used polar activators are propylene carbonate, methanol/water and ethanol/water mixture. Acetone is an excellent polar activator but it is seldom used today due to safety and environmental concerns. Several other low molecular alcohols are also used as polar activators in the industry. While all the polar activators are highly efficient, the methanol/water or ethanol/water combinations are most frequently used due to cost considerations in paint formulation, however, propylene carbonate/water mixture is best suitable for formulating high temperature resistant greases. An optimum amount of polar (chemical) activator must be used to avoid problem of reduction in gel strength. If not enough polar activator is used, then even with the application of shear not all the platelets will be wedged apart. This will result in partial delamination and inadequate gel strength as shown in Figure 1.12a, b.

An excessive level of polar activator interferes with hydrogen bonding and weakens the gelation forces leading to a reduction in gel strength [60-61]. It should also be noted that when using an alcohol as a polar activator,

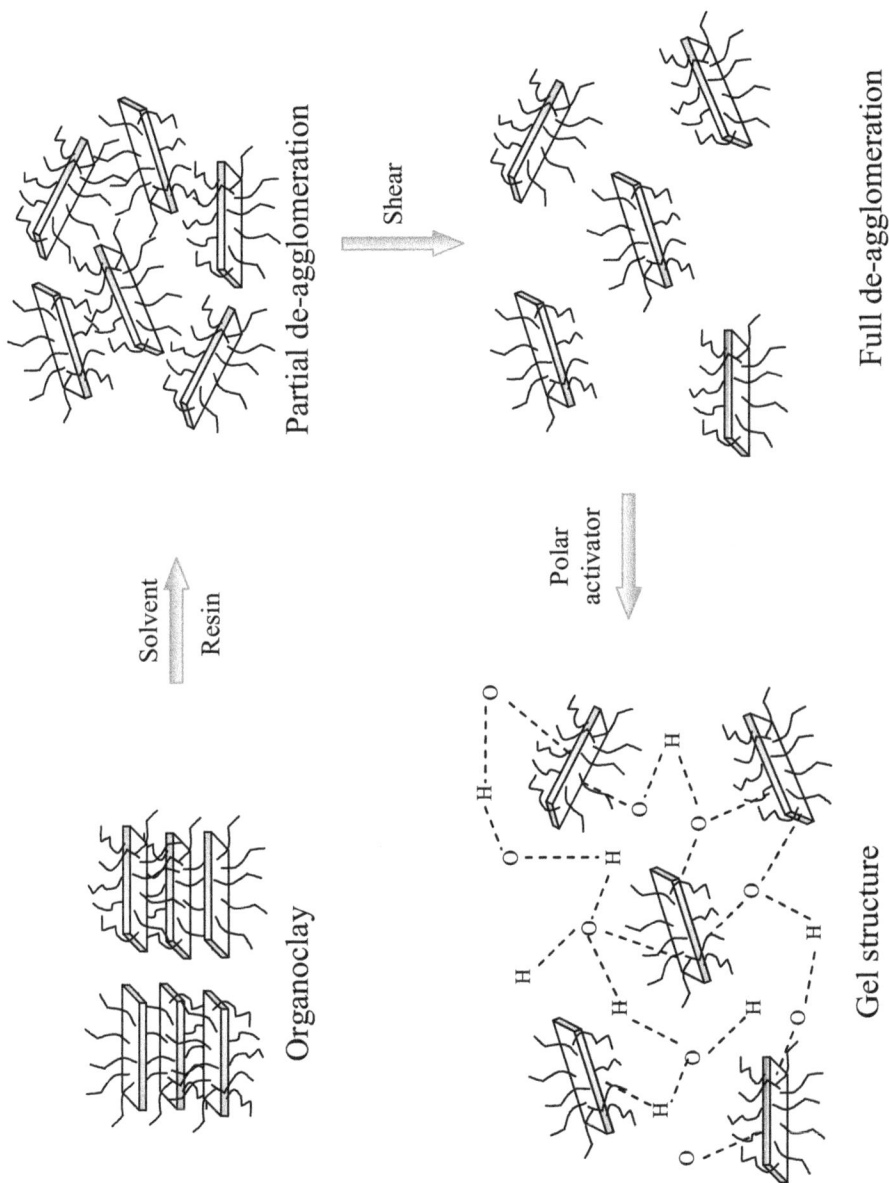

Partial de-agglomeration

Full de-agglomeration

Shear

Solvent

Resin

Polar activator

Organoclay

Gel structure

Figure 1.11. Mechanism of gel formation.

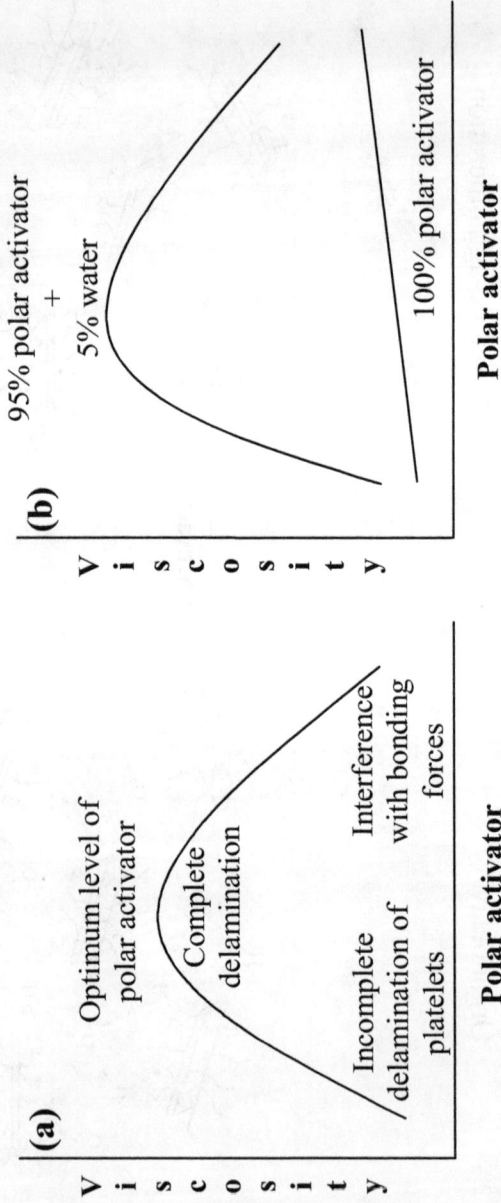

Figure 1.12. (a) Effect of amount of polar activator on viscosity, and **(b)** effect of polar activator/water on viscosity of fluid system.

it must contain at least 5 per cent water. If water is absent, the polar activator will not function efficiently, thus reducing final product performance. Poor gel strength development without the water addition indicates that not enough water molecules were available to form a bridge between the hydroxyls on organoclay platelet edges. There are three main types of mechanisms that occur while adding organoclay into solvent based system: hydrogen bridging or OH-bonds formation, associativity space orientation which results into gel structure as shown in Figure 1.11. The rheological properties of the paint system are enhanced by small addition of organoclays either by pre-gel or dry addition as discussed above. The gel formation prevents pigment settling and sagging on vertical surfaces to ensure that the proper thickness of the coating is applied. They also ensure good leveling for the removal of brush marks and storage stability even with high temperatures. Organoclay is also used in the ink formulation. It helps to adjust the consistency of printing inks to the desired level, avoiding pigment sedimentation, providing good color distribution, obtaining desired film thickness, reduction in misting, control of tack, water pickup and dot gain control by incorporation of small amount of organically modified layered silicates. Thickening lubricating oils with organoclays can produce especially high temperature resistant lubricating greases. Organoclay also gives good working stability and water resistance to the greases. Such greases are typically used for lubrication in foundries, mills and on high-speed conveyors, agriculture, automotive and mining. Likewise, the performance of cosmetics is also enhanced by the use of organoclays and they allow good color retention and coverage for nail lacquers, lipsticks and eye shadows. They have been tested to be nonirritant for both skin and eye contact [59, 62].

1.4. Nanoclays for adsorption of toxic molecules

The organic cation binds to the ionic surfaces of layered silicates and converts it from a hydrophilic form to an oil-wet, a hydrocarbon adsorbent material, ideal for water treatment applications. When used for water treatment, organoclays are commonly utilized in the upstream sector of the petroleum industry for removing hydrocarbons from refinery process water. Organoclays have also been tested for treating ground and surface water and for other toxic organic chemicals from pharmaceuticals and pesticides industries. Organoclays can offer dramatic performance improvements in many other adsorption applications, including removing oil, grease, heavy metals and polychlorinated biphenyl; organic matter, such as humic and fulvic acids; polynuclear and polycyclic aromatics; and sparingly soluble hydrophobic, chlorinated organics. Removing radionuclides, including pertechnetate, from water is another application with tremendous potential [63-67].

Humic acid is one of the common contaminant in potable water and is difficult to remove with conventional flocculation techniques commonly used for drinking water treatment and activated carbon is very ineffective due to its weak interaction with humic acid. The comparative studies for removal efficiencies of humic acid from ground water using different sorbents are shown in Figure 1.13. The use of organoclays in wastewater treatment has become common in industry today. Organoclays exhibit a synergistic effect with many commonly utilized water treatment unit processes including granular-activated charcoal, reverse osmosis and air

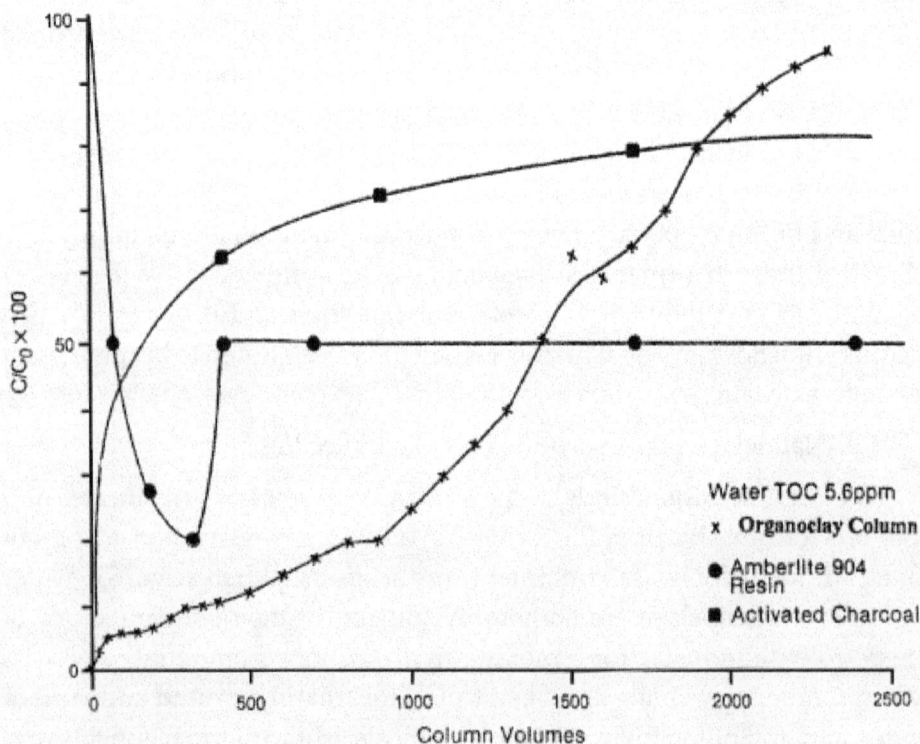

Figure 1.13. Removal efficiencies of humic acid by different sorbents [68].

strippers. Granular-activated carbon is particularly effective at removing a large range of organic molecules from water, however, is very poor for removing large molecules such as humic acid and wastewater containing emulsified oil and grease. Organoclays have proven to be the technology of choice for treating oily wastewaters [68].

Partitioning is the mechanism responsible for the sorption of organics by organoclays. The organoclay contains alternating organic and inorganic layers. The organic layer is comprised of the quaternary ammonium compounds ion exchanged on the surface. This hydrophobic layer acts as an organic phase into which organic substances that are dissolved in water can partition. The partitioning efficiency should be a function of water solubility of the organic substance since the two phases available to it are water and the quaternary compound in the gallery of the clay. Organoclay is one of the ideal material for treating industrial waste water. In the process of manufacturing heater coils, as part of their quality control (QC), the company leak tests each unit. The leak testing is conducted by pressurizing the coils while they are submersed in large tanks of water. Since the leaks are spotted visually, the water in the tanks must be as clear as possible. As more and more coils are tested, residual oil utilized in the manufacturing process builds up in the water, causing the turbidity to climb rapidly. In the past, the test tanks required frequent dumping and refilling, causing problems with discharge of the oily water and the expense of additional water to refill the test tanks. In the initial testing of treatment alternatives for this water, three processes were studied which included pH adjustment, alum flocculation and organoclay column treatment. It was found that pH adjustment was totally ineffective. The alum flocculation test worked reasonably well; however, this process required substantial outlays for equipment and allocation of space, plus a solid waste stream would be produced requiring disposal [69].

The disposal of such sludges is becoming increasingly more difficult and expensive. The disposal of such waste also leaves the waste generator with a potential long-term liability. The best alternative tested was column treatment of the waste with organoclay. A comparison of the results obtained from the alum/NaOH/polymer flocculation and organoclay column test is shown in Table 1.4. As can be seen in the results, the organoclay treatment yielded superior clarity and oil and grease removal when compared to the alum treatment. In addition to leak test tank waste water treatment, organoclays can be extensively used to treat military base effluent, oil well acid returns, boiler feed water, steam condensate among others.

Table 1.4. Comparison of alum flocculation and organoclay treatment [68].

Type Sample	pH	Turbidity (NTU)	Oil and Grease (ppm)	Appearance
Untreated water (a)	6.6	18.0	52	Turbid
(a) Treated with alum-NaOH-Polymer	8.0	0.4	32	Clear
Untreated water (b)	7.1	15.0	62	Turbid
(b) Treated with organoclay	7.1	0.4	2	Clear

1.5. Nanoclays for Supporting Metal Nanoparticles

Heterogeneous catalysis is attracting more attention because of the increasing environmental requirements on waste minimization [70-71]. Metallic nanoparticles are known to present a very high catalytic activity towards a wide range of applications. However, both their recovery and recycling are often difficult. One solution to this problem consists of anchoring the metallic nanoparticles on a solid supports. Nowadays, the most commonly used form of supported metal nanoparticles is activated carbon. Apart from activated carbon, there are several supports reported as supporting materials for growing metal nanoparticles and these are widely used as heterogeneous catalysts in industries as well as academia [72-76]. However, activated carbon is microporous, which reduces the diffusion of the substrates towards the active particles. In this context, the design of new catalytic supports bearing both metallic nanoparticles and a hierarchical porosity that combines a macroporous structure (for good accessibility) with microporous domains (for a large specific surface area) could be a significant improvement.

The preparation and catalytic application of clay–intercalated metal complexes and nanoparticles, initiated by Pinnavaia *et al.* [77-78], have attracted considerable attention. One of the most widely used support materials, montmorillonite, belongs to the group of smectite clay minerals. Metal insertion may be enhanced by utilizing the swelling property of montmorillonite; *i.e.*, the application of an appropriate dispersion medium gives rise to expansion of the clay lamellae and hence results in an increased basal spacing available for guest species. Smectite clays find applications in heterogeneous catalysis as catalysts or catalyst supports. There are two major classes: pillared clays and metal complex-layered silicate intercalation catalysts. For the latter type, transition metal complexes as homogeneous catalysts have been immobilized in the interlamellar space of layer silicates and used in liquid phase hydrogenation reactions [79]. The major advantage of these transition metal-clay mineral catalysts is that the interlayer distance changes as the composition of the reaction medium is changed; therefore, stereo-specific reactions can be performed. In a further step, the catalytically active metal ions can be reduced to zero valent metal allowing not only liquid-phase but also gas phase catalytic reactions to be performed [80].

Dekany's group studied [81-85] palladium, rhodium and platinum metal nanoparticles supported on montmorillonite by preparation of these nanoparticles in quaternary ammonium salts, subsequently exchanged with montmorillonite. The organic-inorganic hybrid formed acts as a nano-phase reactor which controls and stabilizes the metal/metal oxide nanoparticles. These organophilic materials proved to be efficient catalysts in liquid-phase hydrogenation reactions of alkenes. Mastalir *et al.,* [86] reported preparation of organophilic Pd–MMT catalyst for alkyne semihydrogenation. They incorporated palladium nanoparticles into organophilic montmorillonite (Pd-MMT) mediated by a cationic surfactant stabilizer. The proposed mechanism for the successive formation of the Pd hydrosol and the Pd-MMT is illustrated in Figure 1.14. The apolar system $Pd(acac)_2$ dissolved in $CHCl_3$ is situated in the internal apolar part of the micelles formed in the aqueous solution. The addition of an aqueous hydrazine solution to the micellar system resulted in the formation of Pd^0 nanoparticles, stabilized both sterically and electrostatically by the cationic surfactant molecules adsorbed on the surface of the particles.

The stabilizing effect of the alkylammonium molecules prevented the aggregation of nanosized Pd clusters. Pd–MMT was obtained by mixing the Pd hydrosol with a dilute Na–MMT suspension. The reaction of Na–MMT with the stabilizing surfactant molecules resulted in the formation of organophilic alkylammonium MMT, with the simultaneous release and the subsequent deposition of the Pd nanoparticles on the surface of the

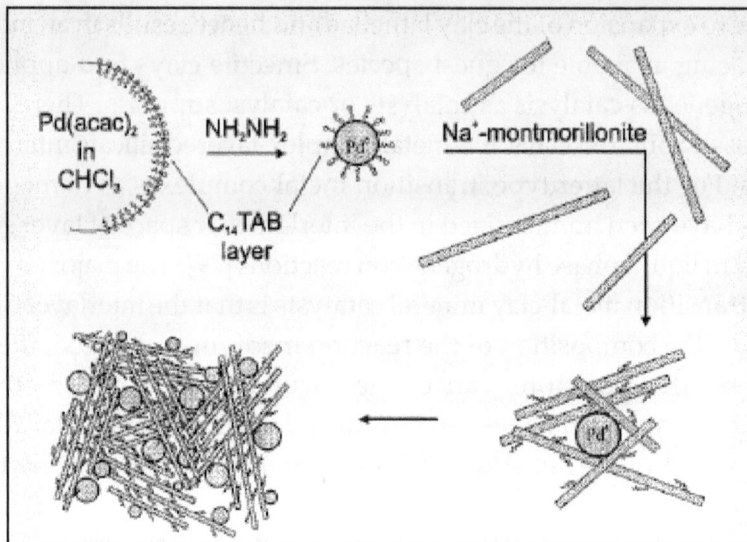

Figure 1.14. Schematic illustration of the mechanism suggested for the successive formation of Pd hydrosol and Pd–MMT in a micellar system.

clay lamellae. It should be stressed that the surfactant molecules had a key role in the preparation of Pd–MMT since they ensured both the stabilization of the Pd particles and the cationic exchange of the MMT host by rendering it hydrophobic and thus readily applicable in organic media. By this technique Pd metal nanoparticles of 2.42 nm (average particle size) was obtained for the concentration of 0.11 per cent w/w while at higher concentration of Pd (0.42 per cent w/w), the average particle size was observed as 3.68 nm.

Gold is usually considered chemically inert, but nanosized gold particles can be very effective catalysts. This indicates that the catalytic properties of a particular material can be dramatically influenced by the particle size. The observation that gold particles with diameters of about 5 nm or less exhibit unique catalytic properties has led to a search both for an explanation of this quite unexpected effect and for chemical reactions that are catalyzed by gold [87-90]. In some cases, catalysts based on nanosized gold particles allow a significantly lower reaction temperature than used in existing processes, which is promising for the development of energy efficient processes. Silver nanoparticles are also gaining enormous attention due to its antibacterial efficiency and catalytic organic transformations. Synthesis of gold and silver metal nanoparticles involves the reduction of metal salts in surfactant solutions using a reducing agent such as sodium citrate or sodium borohydride. Murphy's research group [91-92] reported seeding growth of gold nanoparticles of various shapes and sizes in quaternary ammonium surfactants.

References

1. Theng B. K. G., 1979, Formation and Properties of Clay-Polymer Complexes, *Elsevier Scientific Publisher*, Amsterdam.

2. Grim R. E., 1953, Clay Mineralogy, *McGrow-Hill Book Co.*, Inc., New York.

3. Grim, R.E., 1962. Applied Clay Mineralogy, *McGrow-Hill Book Co.*, Inc., New York.

4. Theng B.K.G., 1974, The Chemistry of Clay-organic Reactions, *John Wiley and Sons*, Inc., New York.

5. Guven N., 1988, Smectites, In: S.W.Bailey (ed.) Hydrous Phyllosilicates (exclusive of micas) Reviews in Mineralogy, Vol. 19, *Mineralogical Society of America*.

6. Barrer R. M., 1978, Zeolites and Clay Minerals as Sorbents and Molecular Sieves, *Academic Press*, London.

7. Worrall, W. E., 1986, Clays and Ceramic Raw Materials, 2nd Ed., *Elsevier Science Publishers*, Amsterdam.

8. Van Olphane H., 1977, An Introduction to Clay Colloid Chemistry for Clay Technologists, Geologists and Soil Scientists, *John Wiley and Sons*, Inc., New York.

9. Van Olphane H., 1976, Clays, In: Parfitt G. D. and Sing K. S. W. (eds.), Characterization of Powder Surfaces. *Academic Press*, London.

10. Grim R. E. and Guven, N., 1978, Bentonites Geology, Mineralogy, Properties and Uses (Developments in Sedimentology 24), *Elsevier Scientific Publisher*, Amsterdam.

11. Bergava F., Theng B. K. G. and Lagaly G., 2006, Handbook of Clay Science, Ist Edition, *Elsevier Scientific Publisher*, Amsterdam.

12. Patel H. A., Somani R. S., Bajaj H. C. and Jasra R. V., *Curr. Sci.*, 92(7), 1004, 2007.

13. Komadel P., Madejova J. and Bujdak J., *Clays Clay Miner.*, 53(4), 313, 2005.

14. Laird D. A., *Appl. Clay Sci.*, 34, 74, 2006.

15. Koster H. M., *Clay Miner.*, 31, 417, 1996.

16. Mehra O. P. and Jackson M. L., *Clays Clay Miner.*, 32, 557, 1960.

17. Lagaly G. and Ziesmer S., *Adv. Colloi. Inter. Sci.*, 100-102, 105, 2003.

18. Penner D. and Lagaly G., *Appl. Clay Sci.*, 19, 131, 2001.

19. Janek M. and Lagaly G., *Appl. Clay Sci.*, 19, 121, 2001.

20. Bergaya F. and Lagaly G., *Appl. Clay Sci.*, 19, 1, 2001.

21. Patel H. A., Somani R. S., Bajaj H. C. and Jasra R. V., *Appl. Clay Sci.*, 35, 194, 2007.

22. Vaia R. A., Teukolsky R. K. and Giannelis E. P., *Chem. Mater.*, 6, 1017, 1994.

23. Xi Y., Frost R. L. and He H., *J. Colloi. Inter. Scie.*, 305, 150, 2007.

24. Xi Y., Ding Z., He H. and Frost R. L., *Spectro. Acta A*, 61, 515, 2005.

25. Xi Y., Ding Z., He H. and Frost R. L., *J. Colloi. Inter. Sci.*, 277, 116, 2004.

26. Vaia R. A., Price G., Ruth P. N., Nguyen H. T. and Lichtenhan J., *Appl. Clay Sci.*, 15, 67, 1999.

27. Okada A. and Usuki A., *Mater. Sci. Eng.*, 3, 109, 1995.

28. Messersmith P. B. and Giannelis E. P., *Chem. Mater.*, 5, 1064, 1993.

29. Carrado K. A. and Xu L. Q., *Chem. Mater.*, 10, 1440, 1998.

30. Gilman J. W., *Appl. Clay Sci.*, 15, 31, 1999.

31. Wang Z. and Pinnavaia T. J., *Chem. Mater.*, 10, 1820, 1998.

32. Kojima Y., Usuki A., Kawasumi M., Okada A., Kurauchi T. and Kamigaito O., *J. Polym. Sci. Part A: Polym. Chem.*, 31, 983, 1993.

33. Kato M., Usuki A. and Okada A., *J. Appl. Polym. Sci.*, 66, 1781, 1997.

34. Messersmith P. B. and Giannelis E. P., *Chem. Mater.*, 6, 1719, 1994.

35. Kornmann X., Berglund L. A. and Sterte J., *Polym. Eng. Sci.*, 38, 1351, 1998.

36. Lan T. and Pinnavaia T. J., *Chem. Mater.*, 6, 2216, 1994.

37. Lan T., Kaviratna P. D. and Pinnavaia T. J., *Chem. Mater.*, 7, 2144, 1995.

38. Zilg C., Mulhaupt R. and Finter J., *Macromol. Chem. Phys.*, 200, 661, 1999.

39. Patel H. A., Somani R. S., Bajaj H. C. and Jasra R.V., *Bull. Mater. Sci.*, 29(2), 133, 2006.

40. Gao F., *Mater. Today*, 50, November 2004.

41. Jordan J., Jacob K. I., Tannenbaum R., Sharaf M. A. and Jasiuk I., *Sci. Engg. A*, 393, 1, 2005.

42. Beyer G., *Plastics Addit. Compou.*, October 2002.

43. Materials news, *Plastics Addit. Compou.*, September-October 2003.

44. Auto applications of drive commercialization of nanocomposites. *Plastic Addit. Compou.*, January 2002.

45. Cox H., *Presented at 4th World Congress in Nanocomposites*, EMC, San Francisco, 1-3 September 2004.

46. Patterson T., *Presented at 4th World Congress in Nanocomposites*, EMC, San Francisco, 1-3 September 2004.

47. Goldman A. Y. and Copsey C. J., *Presented at 4th World Congress in Nanocomposites*, EMC, San Francisco, 1-3 September 2004.

48. Conway R., *Presented at The Future of Nanomaterials Conference*, Pira, Birmingham, 29-30 June 2004.

49. Radford J., *Presented at The Future of Nanomaterials Conference*, Pira, Birmingham, 29-30 June 2004.

50. Business Communication Co. Inc., *www.bccresearch.com*, March 29, 2004.

51. Fischer H., *Mater. Sci. Engg.*, 23, 763, 2003.

52. Le Baron P. C., Wang Z. and Pinnavaia T. J., *Appl. lay Sci.*, 15, 11, 1999.

53. Manias E., Touny A., Wu L., Strawhecker K., Lu B. and Chung T. C., *Chem. Mater.*, 13, 3516, 2001.

54. James Lee L., Zeng C., Cao X., Han X., Shen J. and Xu G., *Compo. Sci. Techn.*, 65, 2344, 2005.

55. Tjong S. C., *Mater. Sci. Engg. R.*, ASAP, 2006.

56. Ray S. S. and Okamoto M., *Progr. Mater. Sci.*, 50, 962, 2005.

57. Ray S. S. and Okamoto M., *Prog. Polym. Sci.*, 28, 1539, 2003.

58. Edwin S., *US Patent 509859*, 1990.

59. Gadberry J. F, Hoey M. and Powell C. F., *US Patent 5663111*, 1997.

60. Somani R. S, Shukla D. B, Bhalala B. J, Mehta A. S and Jasra R. V, *Technical Report*, Indian Oil Corporation, R&D Centre, Faridabad, 1998.

61. Somani R. S, Shukla D. B and Bhalala B. J., *Indian Patent*, NF No. 572/DEL/2000, 2000.

62. Tatum J. P. and Wright R. C., *US Patent 4752342*, 1988.

63. Slabaugh W. H. and Hanson D. B., *J. Colloid. Int. Sci.*, 29, 460, 1969.

64. Stockmeyer M. R., *Appl. Clay Sci.*, 6, 39, 1991.

65. Irene M. C. and Raymond K. M., *Water Sci. Technol.*, 38, 143, 1998.

66. Sanchez-Martin M. J, Rodriguez-Cruz M. S, Andrades M. S. and Sanchez-Camazano M., *Appl. Clay Sci.*, 31, 216, 2005.

67. Jasra R. V., Bajaj H. C. and Mody H. M., *Bull. Cat. Soc.*, 9, 113, 1999.

68. Speed M. A., Barnard A., Arber R. P., Budd G. C. and Johns F. J., *EPA 600 S2-87 011*, 1987.

69. Beall G. W., *Appl. Clay Sci.*, 24, 11, 2003.

70. Daniel M. C. and Astruc D., *Chem. Rev.*, 104, 293, 2004.

71. Rao C. N. R., Kulkarni G. U., Thomas P. J. and Edwards P. P., *Chem. Soc. Rev.*, 29, 27, 2000.

72. Papp Sz. and Dekany I., *Prog. Collo. Poly. Sci.*, 117, 94, 2001.

73. Jhung S. H., Lee J. H., Lee J. M., Lee J. H., Hong D. Y, Kim M. W. and Chang J. S., *Bull. Korean Chem. Soc.*, 26(4), 563, 2005.

74. Yoon B. and Wai C. M., *J. Am. Chem. Soc.*, 127, 17174, 2005.

75. Gommes C. J., Jong K., Pirard J. P. and Blacher S., *Langmuir*, 21, 12378, 2005.

76. Schulz P. G., Gonzalez M. G., Quincoces C. E. and Gigola C. E., *Ind. Eng. Chem. Res.,* 44, 9020, 2005.

77. Pinnavaia T. J., *Science,* 220, 4595, 1983.

78. Pinnavaia T. J., Raythatha R., Lee J. G., Halloran L. J. and Hoffman J. F., *J. Am. Chem. Soc.,* 101, 6891, 1979.

79. Choudary B. M., Bharathi P., *J. Chem. Soc. Chem. Commun.,* 1505, 1987.

80. Giannelis E. P., Rightor E. G. and Pinnavaia T. J., *J. Am. Chem. Soc.,* 110, 3880, 1988.

81. Dekany I., Turi L. and Kiraly Z., *Appl. Clay Sci.,* 15, 221, 1999.

82. Kiraly Z., Dekany I., Mastalir A. and Bartoky M., *J. Catal.,* 161, 401, 1996.

83. Papp Sz., Szucs A. and Dekany I., *Solid State Ionics,* 141-142, 169, 2001.

84. Papp Sz. and Dekany I., *Collo. Polym. Sci.,* 280, 956, 2002.

85. Kiraly Z., Veisz B., Mastalir A., Razgac Z. and Dekany I., *Chem. Commun.,* 1925, 1999.

86. Mastalir A., Kiraly Z., Szollosi Gy., and Bartok M., *J. Catal.,* 194, 146, 2000.

87. Yan W., Mahurin S. M., Chen B., Overbury S. H. and Dai S., *J. Phys. Chem. B,* 109, 15489, 2005.

88. Carrettin S., McMorn P., Johnston P., Griffin Ken., Kiely C. J. and Hutchings G. *J. Phys. Chem. Chem. Phys.,* 5, 1329, 2003.

89. Aihara N., Torigoe K. and Esumi K., *Langmuir,* 14, 4945, 1998.

90. Prati L. and Rossi M., *J. Catal.,* 176, 552, 1998.

91. Murphy C. J. and Jana N. R., *Adv. Mater.,* 14, 80, 2002.

92. Gou L., Murphy C. J., *Chem. Mater.,* 17, 3668, 2005.

Chapter 2
Beneficiation of Indian Bentonites

2.1. Introduction

As discussed in chapter 1, bentonite is smectite group clay formed from the alteration of siliceous, glass-rich volcanic rocks such as tuffs and ash deposits [1-5]. The major mineral in bentonite is montmorillonite. Bentonite is used in a wide range of applications such as drilling mud, foundry sand binding, iron-ore pelletizing and civil engineering uses such as waterproofing and sealant [6-7]. Bentonite has excellent rheological and adsorption properties. Sodium bentonite has a high swelling capacity and forms gel-like masses when added to water. Calcium bentonite has a lower swelling capacity than sodium bentonite [8-10]. The significance of bentonite has increased due to its ability to form organically modified clays or nanoclays, which are gaining a large market place in the field of polymer nanocomposites, paints, greases, inks, cosmetics, wastewater treatment and drug-delivery vehicle in the last decade [11].

The largest sodium bentonite deposits are located in Western United States in Wyoming, Montana and South Dakota. These sodium bentonites are also called Western or Wyoming bentonite, which indicates high-swelling sodium bentonite [9]. Other smaller sodium bentonite deposits occur in Argentina, Canada, China, Greece, Georgia Republic, Morocco, South Africa, Spain and India [12-13]. Bentonite found in the Rajasthan and Gujarat in India is different from that available in the rest of world in terms of its chemical composition and higher iron content, which gives it a brownish-yellow color. Purity of bentonite plays a crucial role in many applications, especially polymer nanocomposites, drug delivery vehicle and cosmetics. Organoclays or nanoclays synthesized from impure bentonite show haziness in polymer nanocomposite films and also limited exfoliation of layered silicates during processing of nanocomposites.

In this chapter, we have beneficiated Indian bentonites of three different origins for improving its physico-chemical properties. There are various methods used for the beneficiation of bentonites, such as chemical treatment, centrifugation, hydrocyclone and sedimentation techniques. In the present study, we have used sedimentation technique governed by Stoke's Law and chemical treatment to purified bentonite. Firstly, the non clay impurities present in the raw bentonite were removed by sedimentation and then purified fraction of bentonites were treated with organic as well as inorganic acids to improve whiteness/glossiness of the purified bentonite.

2.2. Experimental Section

2.2.1. Materials

The raw bentonite lumps were collected from Barmer district (RB), Rajasthan and Kutch district (GK), Gujarat. Sulfuric acid (98 per cent), hydrochloric acid (35 per cent), Sodium hypochlorite (13 per cent), hydrogen peroxide (40 per cent), oxalic acid (99 per cent), citric acid, anhydrous (99 per cent), sodium dithionite (98 per cent) were purchased from s. d. fine Chem., India.

2.2.2. Determination of chemical composition

The chemical composition of the raw, purified and chemically treated samples was measured by gravimetric method and inductively coupled plasma-atomic emission spectroscopy (ICP-AES) [14-15]. The clay samples (~0.5 g) were digested in NaOH or KOH in Ni – crucible at 700 °C for 15 min. The digested mass was purged in the 500 mL of 1:1 hydrochloric acid solution in distilled water. The solution was make up to 500 mL in volumetric flask and was used for the estimation of SiO_2, Al_2O_3, Fe_2O_3, TiO_2, MgO, CaO, Na_2O and K_2O either by gravimetric or ICP-AES analysis. The moisture content of the clays was measured by the difference in weight before and after oven dried clay at 110 °C for 5 h. The Loss on ignition (LOI) was measured by the difference in weight before and after heating the clay samples at 850 °C for 2 h.

2.2.3. Cation Exchange Capacity

There are different methods used for the determination of cation exchange capacity [16-18]. Cation exchange capacity of the samples was measured using standard ammonium acetate method at pH 7.0. About 1.0 g of clay sample was added to the conical flask contained 100 mL of 1M ammonium acetate solution (pH 7.0) and stirred for 2 hrs at room temperature (30 °C). The solution is then kept for 30 min to settle down the clay particles and supernant was filtered through Whatmann filter paper (41). Again, 50 mL of 1M ammonium acetate solution (pH 7.0), stirred for 2 hrs at room temperature (30 °C) and after 30 min. supernant was filtered out. These processes were repeated 6-7 times to obtained NH_4^+-clay from Na^+, Ca^{2+} or K^+- clay. Finally, the NH_4^+-clay was filtered and washed by methanol until free from excess ammonium ions as tested by Nessler's reagent. The NH_4^+-clay was digested in 500 mL round bottom flask containing 20 mL of 40 per cent KOH solution and 230 mL distilled water at 80-90 °C for 1h. During the digestion, NH_4^+- clay is converted to K^+ - clay and liberated ammonia is condensed and neutralized by 25 mL of 0.1N H_2SO_4 solution as shown in Figure 2.1 (experimental set-up for the determination of CEC). The neutralized H_2SO_4 solution was titrated with 0.1n NaOH solution and the difference in the concentration is a measured of CEC as;

$$\text{Cation Exchange Capacity (CEC),} \atop \text{meq/100 g of clay} = \frac{(Vb - Vs) \times N1 \times 100}{W}$$

where,

Vb is blank reading, Vs is sample reading, N1 is normality of NaOH and W is the weight of the clay in gram.

2.2.4. Beneficiation of Bentonite by Sedimentation

Purified bentonite fractions were obtained by dispersing 50, 100, 200, 300 and 400 g of raw bentonite lumps (RB; collected from Barmer district)

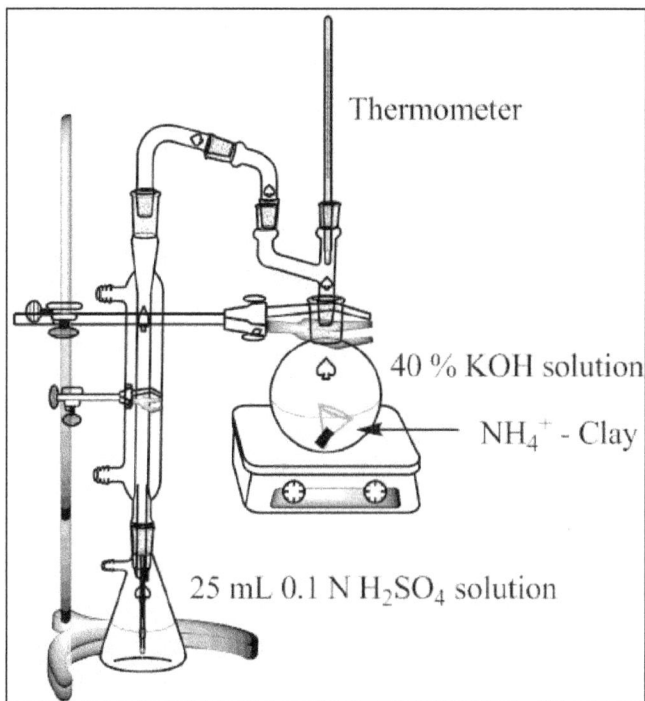

Figure 2.1. Experimental set-up for the determination of cation exchange capacity of clays.

in different buckets containing 10 L of distilled water (0.5, 1, 2, 3 and 4 per cent clay slurry), and allowed to swell overnight, and then stirred for 30 min. According to the Stoke's law of sedimentation, the supernatant slurry having desired clay particle size (< 2 μm) was collected after the pre-calculated time (10 h) and height (15 cm) at room temperature (30°C). The bentonite slurry was then dried at 90 °C, ground, sieved through 200 mesh and designated as RP0.5, RP1, RP2, RP3 and RP4 respectively. The same procedure was employed for bentonite lumps collected from Kutch district, which were designated as GKP0.5, GKP1, GKP2, GKP3 and GKP4.

2.2.5. Chemical Treatment of Purified Bentonite

27.8 mL H_2SO_4 (1N), 83.4 mL H_2SO_4 (3N), 90 mL HCl (1N), 270 mL HCl (3N), 270 mL HCl (3N) and 25 mL H_2O_2 (1 per cent), 569.2 mL NaOCl (1N), 6.3 g oxalic acid (0.1M), 12.6 g oxalic acid (0.2M), 6.4 g citric acid (0.1M) and 10 g sodium dithionite were each added in separate 2 L beakers and made up to 1L with deionized water. In each solution, 10g of purified bentonite (RP) was added and heated at 80-90 C for 2 hrs with continuous stirring, cooled, filtered, washed with deionized water, dried and powdered. The chemically treated clays thus obtained were designated as RPC-1, RPC-2, RPC-3, RPC-4, RPC-5, RPC-6, RPC-7, RPC-8, RPC-9 and RPC-10 respectively as shown in Table 2.1.

Table 2.1. Chemical treatment of purified bentonite.

Sl.No.	Chemical Treatment (Treatment were carried out at 80-90 C for 2 h)	Sample Name
1.	1N H_2SO_4	**RPC-1**
2.	3N H_2SO_4	**RPC-2**
3.	1N HCl	**RPC-3**
4.	3N HCl	**RPC-4**
5.	3N HCl + 1 per cent H_2O_2	**RPC-5**
6.	1N NaOCl	**RPC-6**
7.	0.1M Oxalic acid	**RPC-7**
8.	0.2 M Oxalic acid	**RPC-8**
9.	0.1 M Citric acid	**RPC-9**
10.	1:1 Sodium dithionite	**RPC-10**

2.2.6. Characterization

CEC of raw bentonite (RB, GK) and purified bentonite (RP0.5, RP1, RP2, RP3 and RP4; GKP0.5, GKP1, GKP2, GKP3 and GKP4) samples measured using standard ammonium acetate method at pH 7.0, montmorillonite content by cylinder enrichment (CE) method [18]. In the CE method, 15 g of purified bentonite samples was dispersed in 1 L deionized water using ultrasonic dispersion. The suspension was transferred into 1 L glass cylinders (diameter ~5 cm) and kept in an oven at 60 °C until the water is evaporated. From the top side of the sediment, 0.5 g of sample from each cylinder was removed using a sharp knife. These materials were equilibrated for 7 days at 50–60 per cent relative humidity in order to regain the expansion capacity. Finally, the CEC was determined using standard ammonium acetate method and montmorillonite content (per cent w/w) with respect to its original CEC of purified samples was calculated. Swelling volume was measured by dispersing 1 g of clays in cylinder contained 100 mL distilled water. The cylinders were kept for 24 hrs and the swelling volume was noted as cm³. The whiteness of untreated, treated montmorillonite and organoclays with reference to magnesium carbonate block were measured by *PEI* Digital reflectance meter. Powder X-ray diffraction (PXRD) analysis was carried out with a Phillips powder diffractometer *X' Pert MPD* using PW3123/00 curved Cu-filtered Cu-Kα (λ=1.54056) radiation with slow scan of 0.3 degree/second in 2-70 2θ degree for raw, purified and chemically treated bentonite. Fourier transform infrared spectra (FT-IR) of raw and purified bentonites were measured with Perkin-Elmer Spectrum GX-Spectrophotometer as KBr pellet.

2.3. Results and Discussion

2.3.1. Sedimentation of Indian Bentonite

We have used Indian bentonites of Barmer district (RB), Rajasthan and Kutch district (GK), Gujarat. The Chemical composition of bentonite obtained from these different regions is shown in Table 2.2. Chemical analysis of raw and purified bentonite samples indicates the removal of excessive nonclay impurities by sedimentation carried out with lower concentration and thus lower viscosity. The amount of ferric oxide decreases up to about 9.2 wt per cent (RB0.5) and 9.4 wt per cent (GK0.5) from 10.3 wt per cent (RB) and 11.2 wt per cent (GK). However the titania in bentonite of Rajasthan origin is not beyond detectable limit, the bentonite collected from the Kutch (GK), Gujarat having titania and was remained unchanged by sedimentation. Purification of clay minerals using different inorganic and organic acids has been reported in literature [19-27]. Chemical analysis, CEC and montmorillonite content of the different samples clearly demonstrate that sedimentation carried out at lower weight percentage of clay (RB0.5, RB1 and RB2) yields bentonite free from nonclay impurities. Chemical analysis, CEC and montmorillonite content of the different samples clearly demonstrate that sedimentation carried out at lower weight percentage of clay (RB0.5, RB1 and RB2) yields bentonite free from nonclay impurities. As the concentration of clay increases, the viscosity of clay slurry increases which in turn makes sedimentation of the non-clay particles (greater than 2 mm) difficult. Montmorillonite content (89 per cent w/w) and swelling volume (24 cm³) of samples purified by sedimentation at lower concentration (RB0.5 and

Table 2.2. Chemical composition of raw and purified bentonite samples.

Chemical Composition (per cent w/w)	LOI	SiO$_2$	Al$_2$O$_3$	Fe$_2$O$_3$	TiO$_2$	CaO	MgO	Na$_2$O	K$_2$O	Total
RB (raw)	10.7	56.3	17.2	10.3	N/D	1.9	2.1	0.6	0.4	99.5
RB4	8.1	57.6	17.3	10.1	N/D	2.1	2.8	0.9	1.3	100.2
RB3	8.4	56.8	17.6	9.8	N/D	2.1	2.6	0.8	1.1	99.2
RB2	8.8	57.1	17.3	9.5	N/D	1.9	2.6	0.8	1.1	99.1
RB1	8.9	57.5	17.4	9.2	N/D	1.6	2.9	0.9	0.8	99.2
RB0.5	8.5	57.8	17.5	9.2	N/D	1.9	2.8	0.8	0.8	99.3
GK	9.5	56.7	16.4	11.2	1.8	1.9	1.2	0.9	0.4	100
GK4	7.5	56.7	18.5	10.6	1.8	1.5	1.3	0.9	0.7	99.4
GK3	7.7	56.5	18.3	10.1	1.8	1.5	1.5	1.1	0.8	99.3
GK2	7.6	55.9	19.2	9.8	1.8	1.5	1.6	1.1	0.8	99.3
GK1	7.8	55.9	20.2	9.4	1.8	1.5	1.5	1.1	0.8	100
GK0.5	7.7	55.9	20.3	9.4	1.5	1.5	1.7	1.2	0.8	100

RB1) is higher compared to raw and purified bentonites at higher concentration (RB2, RB3 and RB4) as shown in Table 2.3. The brightness indices of purified bentonite obtained by sedimentation at lower concentration (RB0.5, RB1) is also higher (60) compared to raw and purified bentonites at higher concentration (RB, RB4, RB3 and RB2). This is due to the removal of excessive iron-stained impurities which are responsible for the brownish-yellow color of bentonite and is also evident from chemical composition as shown in Table 2.2.

Table 2.3. Cation exchange capacity (CEC) and montmorillonite (MMT) content, swelling volume and brightness indices of raw and purified bentonite samples.

Sample	CEC	CEC by CE Method	MMT Content (per cent w/w)	Swelling Volume (cm³)	Brightness Index
RB	71	–	–	16	54
RB4	72	88	81	16	55
RB3	75	93	81	17	55
RB2	85	97	87	21	57
RB1	90	101	89	24	60
RB0.5	90	101	89	24	60
GK	72	–	–	21	53
GK4	72	88	81	21	53
GK3	77	91	84	21	53
GK2	87	97	90	25	56
GK1	90	101	89	29	58
GK0.5	90	101	89	29	58

The CEC of the clay samples also increases with decrease in the concentration of the clay in water. Similar trends in MMT content, CEC and brightness index were observed from the sedimentation study carried out using bentonite collected from the Kutch (GK), Gujarat. Moisture content of all samples varies between 7 and 9 wt per cent and depends on the relative humidity during samples analysis. Loss on ignition which is carried out at 850 °C in air atmosphere remains almost similar for all samples. Quartz and calcite impurities are also removed during sedimentation up to 3 per cent clay slurry, which also correlated with FT-IR and PXRD.

2.3.1.1. FTIR and PXRD Study of Raw and Purified Bentonites

FT-IR spectra of raw and purified bentonite samples recorded in the range 500–1050 cm^{-1} to study the effect of clay concentration during sedimentation technique are shown in Figure 2.2. IR peaks at 915, 875 and 793 cm^{-1} are attributed to AlAlOH, AlFeOH and platy form of tridymite bending vibration respectively.

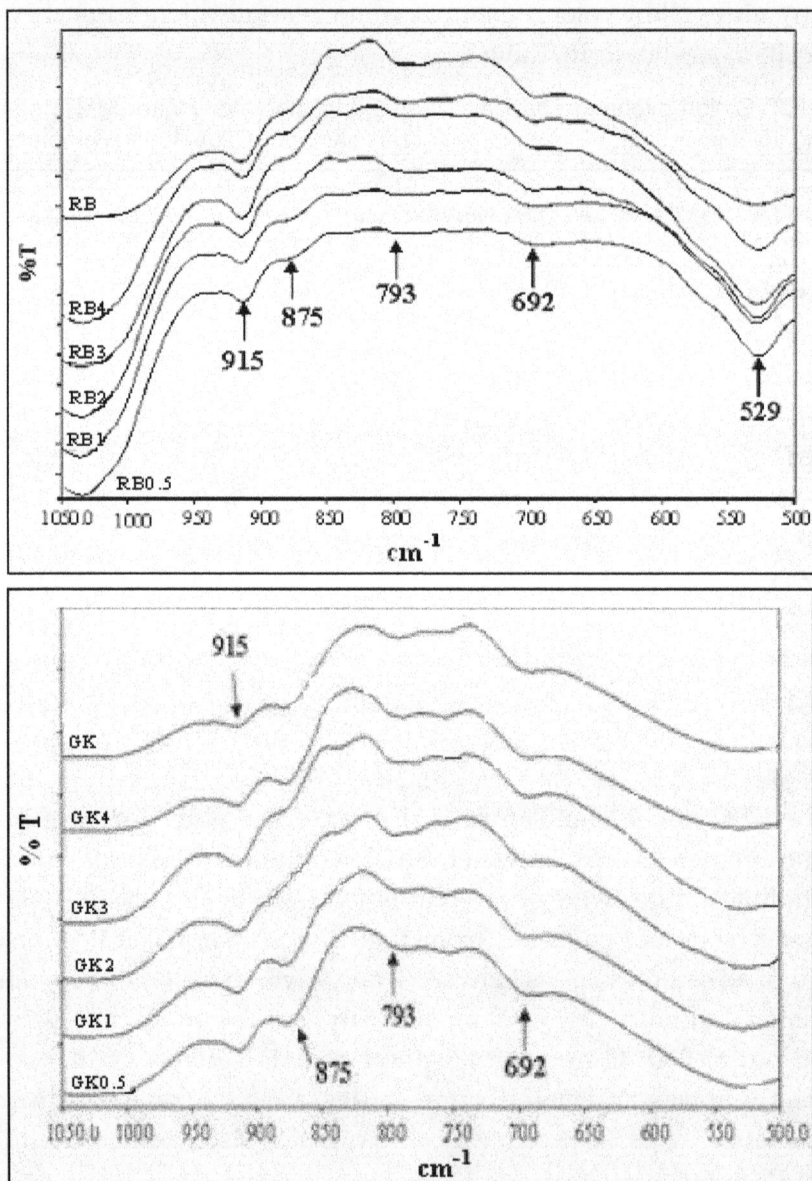

Figure 2.2. FTIR spectra of raw and purified bentonite samples.

The characteristic peak at 1115 cm⁻¹ is due to Si–O stretching, out-of-plane Si–O stretching mode for MMT. The band at 1035 cm⁻¹ is attributed to Si–O stretching (in-plane) vibration for layered silicates. Intensity of vibrational peak at 915 (AlAlOH) and 529 cm⁻¹ (Si–O bending) increases as the concentration of clay slurry decreases, which indicates an increase in MMT content. Intensity of vibrational peak at 875 (AlFeOH) and 692 cm⁻¹ (quartz) decreases and tends to diminish for lower clay concentration (RB0.5 and RB1), confirming the removal of iron-stained impurities and free silica from bentonite.

The PXRD pattern (Figure 2.3 *a–c*) indicates the presence of impurities such as kaolin (K), quartz (Q) and calcite (Ca) in raw as well as purified bentonite samples, which are partly or to a great extent removed on further purification by sedimentation. Most of the quartz and calcite impurities are removed after sedimentation at 2 wt per cent clay slurry. There is no change in kaolin peak intensity, probably due to its fine particles and also less swelling ability of kaolinite mineral. Reflections relative to the planes [001], [003] and [130–200] confirmed the presence of MMT with d_{001} ~ 1.2 nm for samples GK and RB, indicating the presence of Na-MMT. It is clear from the PXRD pattern that sedimentation carried out by dispersing more than 2 wt per cent bentonite in deionized water is not able to remove non-clay impurities due to higher viscosity of the clay slurry.

Table 2.4. Upgradation parameters to obtained purified bentonite at different temperature.

Temperature (C)	Height after 24 h	
	1μm	*2μm*
15	6.6	26.4
20	7.5	30.0
25	8.4	33.8
30	9.4	37.7
35	10.5	41.8
40	11.5	46.1
45	12.6	50.4

Therefore, it is preferred to suspend a lower amount of bentonite in deionized water for better beneficiation. It was observed during chemical

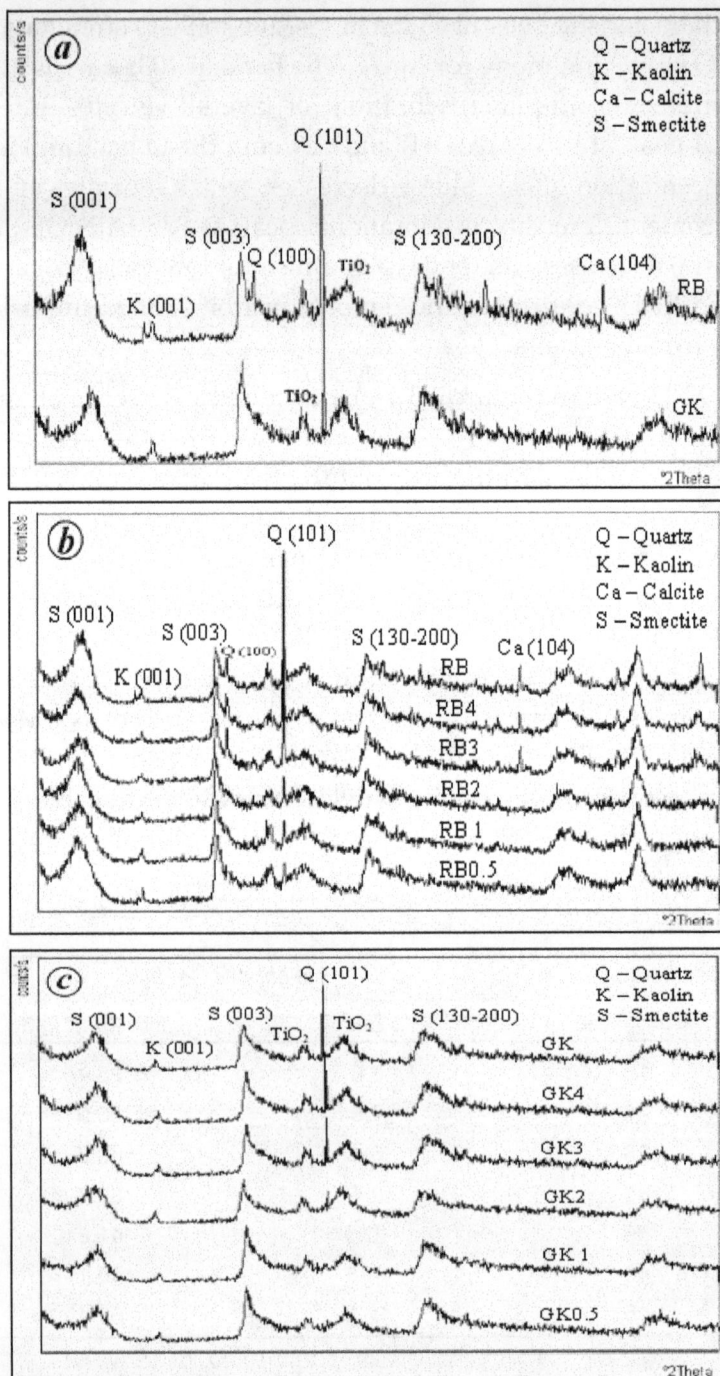

Figure 2.3. Powder X-ray diffraction patterns: *a*, Raw bentonite, Kutch district (GK) and Barmer district (RB); *b*, Raw bentonite (RB) and purified bentonite (RB0.5- RB4), and *c*, Raw bentonite (GK) and purified bentonite (GK0.5- GK4).

analysis that the chemical composition is varying with sample to sample and thus average of chemical composition of three samples was reported.

Chemical composition, CEC, montmorillonite content, swelling indices and brightness indexes clearly indicate that most of the non-clay impurities such as quartz, iron-stained impurities and calcite can be removed from raw bentonite by suspending less than 2 per cent bentonite in deionized water.

We have carried out series of experiment based on the above observations by taking 1.5 per cent w/v bentonite lumps in distilled water and applying Stoke's Law for sedimentation to fix out the parameters such as temperature and height for 24 h time for less than 1 and 2 µm clay particles for rest of the research work in this thesis. The slurry of bentonite lumps in distilled water ($\leq$ 1.5 wt. per cent) were prepared for the upgradation by Stoke's Law of sedimentation and the supernatant (< 2µm or < 1µm fraction) obtained after pre-calculated time, height was collected and used for preparation of organoclays. The upgradation parameters such as temperature, height and time vary with the size of the vessel used for sedimentation as shown in Table 2.4.

The chemical composition of purified fraction of bentonite clay (RP and GKP) obtained from 1.5 per cent w/v bentonite in distilled water is

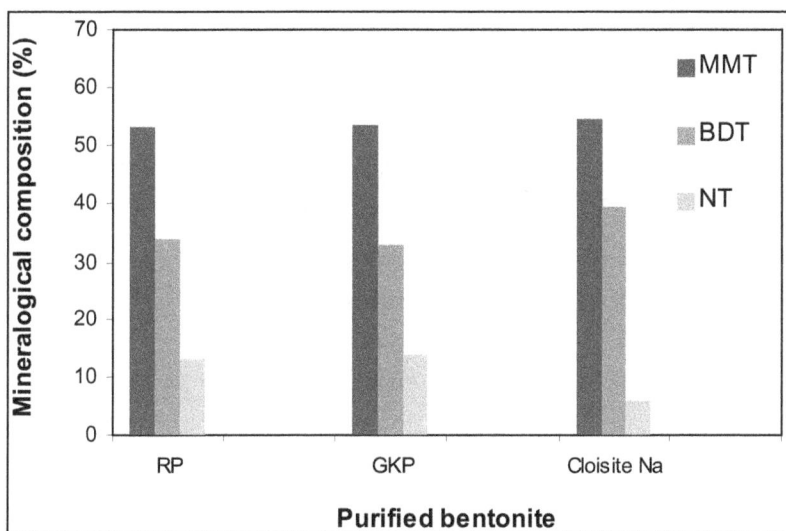

Figure 2.4. Mineralogical content of the purified bentonite (RP and GKP) and imported sample (Cloisite Na).

given in Table 2.5. Titania is present in the GKP and therefore RP was used for the chemical treatment. As shown in Table 2.5, there is only difference in the chemical composition of GKP and RK with Cloisite Na (imported sample; Southern Clay Products) is iron content. If ferric oxide/hydroxide present in the RP and GKP, it could be removed by sedimentation due to its non-swelling capacity. It is clear from the sedimentation study that the iron present in the Indian bentonites is as structural iron (Nontronite, NT) and which is well supported by FTIR spectra.

Table 2.5. Chemical composition of purified bentonite and imported purified bentonite.

Chemical Composition (per cent w/w)	RP	GKP	Cloisite Na
LOI	8.7	8.6	8.5
SiO_2	57.5	56.9	62.6
Al_2O_3	17.4	16.6	18.4
Fe_2O_3	9.2	9.4	5.8
TiO_2	N/D	1.3	N/D
CaO	1.5	2.9	1.5
MgO	2.9	1.8	1.5
Na_2O	0.9	1.5	0.8
K_2O	0.8	0.8	0.9
Total (per cent w/w)	99.3	99.9	100
CEC (meq/100gm)	90	90	92
Moisture content	6.5	6.3	6.4
Brightness index	54	53	81

The calculated ionic formula on the basis of chemical composition of RP, GKP and Cloisite Na is shown in Table 2.7. From the ionic formula, we have derived mineralogical composition (theoretical) as shown in Figure 2.4. The NT is higher in Indian bentonite (12-14 per cent) as compared to Cloisite Na (4-5 per cent). The mineralogical content clearly shows that the brownish-yellow color of Indian bentonite is mainly due to presence of higher amount of NT as compare to Cloisite Na.

2.3.2. Chemical Treatment of Purified Bentonite

The bentonite is treated with organic/inorganic acids to improve brightness and to value-add the clay. Chemical composition and ionic formulas of raw (RB), purified (RP) and chemically treated bentonite (RPC-1 to RPC-10) are shown in Table 2.5 and 2.6. The chemical treatments of clay minerals were improved the brightness of the clays at the cost of their structural leaching [28-29].

The most of the nonclay impurities are removed after purification by sedimentation, CEC and brightness of RP, are increased from 71 to 90meq/g and 48 to 54 respectively. The treatment with 1N and 3N sulfuric acid (RPC-1, RPC-2) improves brightness by 10 and 12 per cent while decreases cation exchange capacity to 10 and 23 per cent respectively, which is due to leaching of tetrahedral silica, octahedral alumina as well as interlayer cations. The treatment with hydrochloric acid also reduces CEC with an improvement in brightness as shown in Table 2.6. The mixture of HCl and hydrogen peroxide removes substantial amount of iron-stained impurities (52 per cent) and improve brightness (12.5 per cent) but at the same time CEC decreases by 30 per cent. There is a negligible improvement in brightness of purified bentonite (RP) by its treatment with 0.1N sodium hypochlorite. There is a slight decrease in the ferric oxide content in the purified bentonite (RP) due to its treatment with organic acids such as oxalic and citric acid, which slightly improves the brightness, however decreases the CEC of the purified (RP) clay.

The sodium dithionite acts as reducing agents for the iron stained impurities. Stucki's group [30-38] have reported several research articles on the basis of iron reduction of Fe-rich bentonite and concluded that the structural iron can not be removed. They have also reported that the nonstructural iron are removed while structural iron reduced during treatment and re-oxidized after some time within the structure. The bentonite treated with sodium dithionite gave best results in terms of removal of iron content (40 per cent) and very little decrease in CEC (6 per cent). The decrease in CEC of chemical treated RP is due to breaking up of the clay structure. The treatments of RP with organic and inorganic acids digest octahedral alumina and isomorphic substituted Mg^{2+} and Fe^{2+}. The interlayer alkaline cations (Na^+, Ca^{2+} and K^+) are also susceptible to acids and leached out during treatment. This observation is also supported by calculated ionic formula (Table 2.7) on the basis of chemical compositions. The mineralogical compositions of chemically treated clays (RPC1-RPC10) are shown in Figure 2.5. The change in the MMT, BDT

Table 2.6. Comparison of chemical composition, CEC and brightness of raw, purified and chemically treated bentonite.

Chemical Composition (per cent w/w)	RPC-1	RPC-2	RPC-3	RPC-4	RPC-5	RPC-6	RPC-7	RPC-8	RPC-9	RPC-10
LOI	10.4	9.8	9.2	8.1	8.5	7.2	9.7	9.8	9.9	10.9
SiO_2	58.3	60.3	57.0	65.6	62.1	58.8	55.7	55.6	56.9	55.8
Al_2O_3	17.9	16.5	21.9	14.9	19.2	18.5	22.6	22.5	21.5	21.9
Fe_2O_3	7.1	6.9	6.8	6.5	4.8	8.5	6.2	6.2	5.6	5.6
CaO	2.4	2.3	1.3	1.4	2.9	2.6	2.4	2.2	2.3	2.4
MgO	2.2	2.5	2.3	2.1	1.5	3.1	1.7	2.1	1.7	1.8
Na_2O	0.7	0.8	0.6	0.6	0.5	0.6	0.7	0.7	0.7	0.7
K_2O	0.9	0.8	0.8	0.7	0.4	0.5	0.8	0.6	0.6	0.6
Total (per cent w/w)	100	100	99.9	99.9	100	99.96	99.9	99.5	99.3	100
CEC(meq/100g)	82	70	71	63	64	82	82	80	78	86
Moisture content	9.44	10.98	10.19	9.94	11.37	11.13	10.1	11.1	10.1	9.43
Brightness	57	68	57	68	68	58	57	55	54	60

and NT content is due to leaching of structural Si, Al, Fe, Mg and exchangeable cations. The NT content decreases with inorganic acid treatment at the cost of structural distortion which in turns reduces CEC of the clays.

Table 2.7. Ionic formula of untreated and treated purified bentonite (RP).

Sample	Ionic Formula
RP	$(Si_{3.87}Al_{0.13})(Al_{1.24}Mg_{0.29}Fe_{0.47})O_{10}(OH)_2$, **X**→ $Na_{0.11}$, $K_{0.08}$, $Ca_{0.11}$
GKP	$(Si_{3.87}Al_{0.13})(Al_{1.19}Mg_{0.19}Fe_{0.49})O_{10}(OH)_2$, **X**→ $Na_{0.19}$, $K_{0.074}$, $Ca_{0.23}$
Cloisite Na	$(Si_4)(Al_{1.45}Mg_{0.17}Fe_{0.22})O_{10}(OH)_2$, **X**→ $Na_{0.12}$, $K_{0.07}$, $Ca_{0.16}$
RPC-1	$(Si_{3.93}Al_{0.07})(Al_{1.35}Mg_{0.23}Fe_{0.35})O_{10}(OH)_2$, **X**→ $Na_{0.10}$, $K_{0.07}$, $Ca_{0.18}$
RPC-2	$(Si_{4.01})(Al_{1.29}Mg_{0.25}Fe_{0.35})O_{10}(OH)_2$, **X**→ $Na_{0.11}$, $K_{0.06}$, $Ca_{0.02}$
RPC-3	$(Si_{3.77}Al_{0.23})(Al_{1.54}Mg_{0.25}Fe_{0.34})O_{10}(OH)_2$, **X**→ $Na_{0.08}$, $K_{0.06}$, $Ca_{0.09}$
RPC-4	$(Si_{4.23})(Al_{1.13}Mg_{0.21}Fe_{0.31})O_{10}(OH)_2$, **X**→ $Na_{0.08}$, $K_{0.06}$, $Ca_{0.09}$
RPC-5	$(Si_{4.027})(Al_{1.46}Mg_{0.145}Fe_{0.23})O_{10}(OH)_2$, **X**→ $Na_{0.06}$, $K_{0.04}$, $Ca_{0.20}$
RPC-6	$(Si_{3.85}Al_{0.15})(Al_{1.28}Mg_{0.29}Fe_{0.42})O_{10}(OH)_2$, **X**→ $Na_{0.12}$, $K_{0.04}$, $Ca_{0.18}$
RPC-7	$(Si_{3.72}Al_{0.28})(Al_{1.5}Mg_{0.17}Fe_{0.31})O_{10}(OH)_2$, **X**→ $Na_{0.10}$, $K_{0.01}$, $Ca_{0.17}$
RPC-8	$(Si_{3.7}Al_{0.3})(Al_{1.47}Mg_{0.22}Fe_{0.31})O_{10}(OH)_2$, **X**→ $Na_{0.10}$, $K_{0.05}$, $Ca_{0.16}$
RPC-9	$(Si_{3.82}Al_{0.18})(Al_{1.51}Mg_{0.17}Fe_{0.28})O_{10}(OH)_2$, **X**→ $Na_{0.10}$, $K_{0.05}$, $Ca_{0.16}$
RPC-10	$(Si_{3.76}Al_{0.24})(Al_{1.5}Mg_{0.185}Fe_{0.28})O_{10}(OH)_2$, **X**→ $Na_{0.10}$, $K_{0.05}$, $Ca_{0.18}$

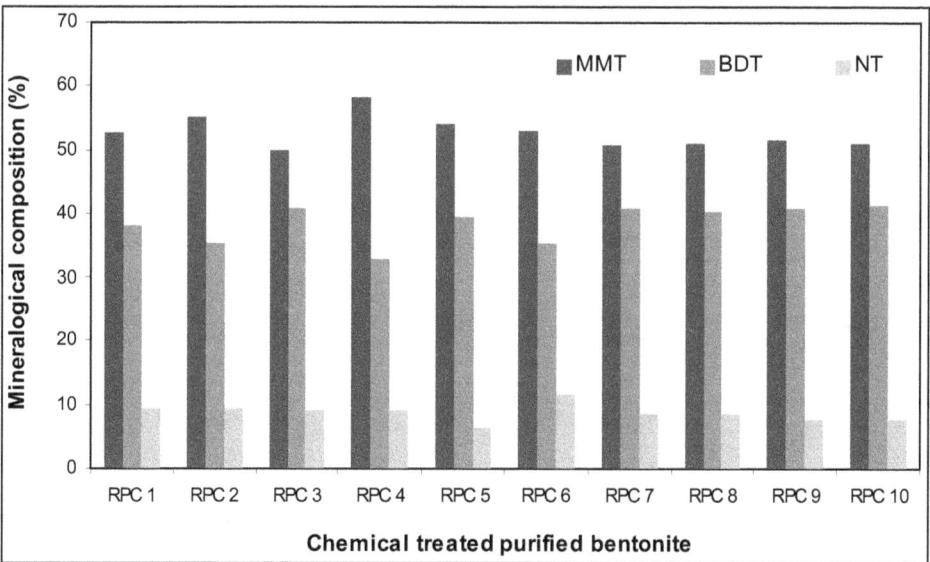

Figure 2.5. Mineralogical content of the chemically treated RP.

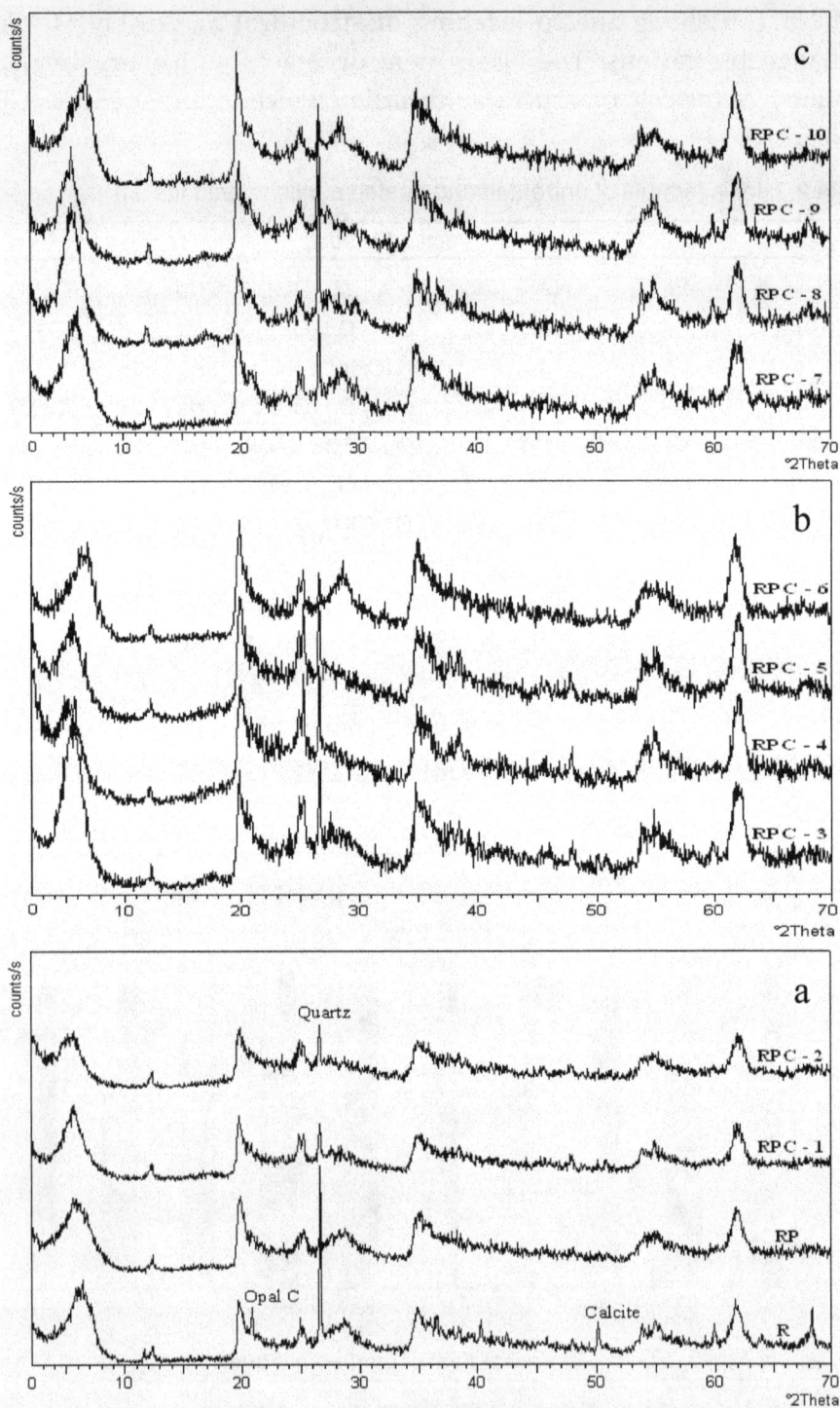

Figure 2.6. PXRD patterns (a, b and c) of raw, purified and chemically treated bentonite.

2.3.2.1. PXRD Studies of Chemically Treated Bentonite

The PXRD patterns of raw, purified and chemically treated bentonite are shown in Figure 2.6a, b and c; the most of the nonclay impurities such as quartz, opal C and calcite present in raw bentonite (RB) are removed after purification by sedimentation (RP). The peak at 21 and 26.5 2θ degree are of opal C [100] and quartz [101] respectively and calcite [104] at 50.5 2θ degree in raw bentonite (RB) which diminishes in RP, indicates that most of the quartz and calcite impurities are removed by purification of bentonite by sedimentation. The bentonite treated with sulfuric acid (RPC-1, RPC-2), hydrochloric acid (RPC-3, RPC-4), mixture of hydrochloric and hydrogen peroxide (RPC-5) and sodium hypochlorite (RPC-6) shows leaching of silica from MMT structure as observed by increase in quartz peak intensity in PXRD pattern of chemically treated bentonite.

Apart from MMT structure, these acids, especially inorganic acids digest octahedral Al, Mg ions and interlayer cations and leave behind free silica, resulted in to MMT with lower CEC (Table 2.6). The ferric oxide content also decreases by treatment of these acids with improvement in whiteness. Though the oxalic acid (RPC-7, RPC-8) and citric acid (RPC-9) have moderately affected MMT structure, they digest interlayer cations which decreases CEC of MMT. The structure of MMT treated with sodium dithionite remains almost unchanged with improvement in brightness and only 6 per cent CEC decreases. The dithionite treatment was carried out without buffer which resulted into acidic pH (4-5) during treatment which affects the structure of MMT and thus reduces its CEC. It is clearly reveals from chemical composition, CEC, ionic formula and PXRD pattern that organic and inorganic acids destroyed the structure of MMT except sodium dithionite. The dithionite treatment removes only non structural iron from the RP. The structural iron reduced from Fe^{3+} to Fe^{2+} and again oxidized while after some time.

References

1. Bergava F., Theng B. K. G. and Lagaly G., 2006, Handbook of Clay Science, Ist Edition, *Elsevier Scientific Publisher*, Amsterdam.

2. Theng B. K. G., 1979, Formation and Properties of Clay-Polymer Complexes, *Elsevier Scientific Publisher*, Amsterdam.

3. Grim R. E., 1953, Clay Mineralogy, *McGrow-Hill Book Co.*, Inc., New York.

4. Grim, R.E., 1962. Applied Clay Mineralogy, *McGrow-Hill Book Co.*, Inc., New York.

5. Theng B.K.G., 1974, The Chemistry of Clay-organic Reactions, *John Wiley and Sons*, Inc., New York.

6. Colin C. H. and Murray H. H., *Appl. Clay Sci.*, 11, 285, 1997.

7. Thorson T. A., *Appl. Clay Sci.*, 11, 329, 1997.

8. Wilson M. J., 1987, Handbook of Determination Methods in Clay Mineralogy, *Chapman and Hall*, New York.

9. Ciullo P. A., 1996, White Bentonite – A Bright Future, *Indust. Miner. Spec. Rev.*, 2nd edn.

10. Grim R. E. and Guven, N., 1978, Bentonites Geology, Mineralogy, Properties and Uses (Developments in Sedimentology 24), *Elsevier Scientific Publisher*, Amsterdam.

11. Patel H. A., Somani R. S., Bajaj H. C. and Jasra R.V., *Bull. Mater. Sci.*, 29(2), 133, 2006.

12. Hassan M. S. and Abdel-Khalek N. A., *Appl. Clay Sci.*, 13, 99, 1998.

13. Colin C. H. and Keeling, J., *Appl. Clay Sci.*, 20, 243, 2002.

14. Worrall, W. E., 1986, Clays and Ceramic Raw Materials, 2nd Ed., *Elsevier Science Publishers*, Amsterdam.

15. Grim R. E. and Guven, N., 1978, Bentonites Geology, Mineralogy, Properties and Uses (Developments in Sedimentology 24), *Elsevier Scientific Publisher*, Amsterdam.

16. Meier L. P. and Kahr G., *Clays Clay Miner.*, 47, 386, 1999.

17. Taylor R. K., *J. Chem. Biotechnol. A*, 35, 195, 1985.

18. Kaufhold S., Dhimann R., Ufer K. and Meyer F. M., *Appl. Clay Sci.*, 22, 145, 2002.

19. Ambikadevi V. R., Gopalakrishna S. J., *Proc. 10th Kerala Scie.*, 1997.

20. Ambikadevi V. R. and Lalithambika M., *Appl. Clay Sci.*, 16, 133, 2000.

21. Bahranowski K., Serwicka E. M., Stoch L. and Strycharski P., *Clay Miner.*, 28, 379, 1993.

22. Conley R. F. and Lloyd M. K., *Ind. Eng. Chem. Process Des. Dev.*, 9 (4), 595, 1970.

23. Mesquita, D., Rodrigues T. And Gomes S. S., *Miner. Eng.*, 9, 965, 1996.

24. Herbillon A. J., Mestidagh M. M., Vielvoye L. and Derouane E. G., *Clay Miner.*, 11, 201, 1976.

25. Hogg C., Malden P. and Meads R., *Mineral. Mag.*, 40, 89, 1975.

26. Veglio F. and Toro L., *Int. J. Miner. Process.*, 41, 239, 1994.

27. Veglio F., Passariello B., Toro L. and Marabini A. M., *Ind. Eng. Chem. Res.*, 35, 1680, 1996.

28. Mandal S. K. and Banerjee P. C., *Int. J. Miner. Process.*, 74, 263, 2004.

29. Saikia N. J., Bharali D. J., Sengupta P., Bordoloi D., Goswamee R. L., Saikia P. C. and Borthakur P. C., *Appl. Clay Sci.*, 24, 93, 2003.

30. Favre F., Bogdal C., Gavillet S. and Stucki J. W., *Appl. Clay Sci.*, 34, 95, 2006.

31. Kandwon L., Kostka J. E. and Stucki J. W., *Clays Clay Miner.*, 54, 195, 2006.

32. Stucki J. W., Kandwon L., Zhang L. and Larson R. A., *Pure Appl. Chem.*, 74, 2145, 2002.

33. Yan L. and Stucki J. W., *Langmuir*, 15, 4648-4657, 1999.

34. Gates W. P., Komadel P., Madejova J. Bujdak J., Stucki J. W. and Kirkpatrick R. J., *Appl. Clay Sci.*, 16, 257, 2000.

35. Fialips C. I., Huo D., Yan L., Wu J. and Stucki J. W., *Clays Clay Miner.*, 50, 455, 2002.

36. Stucki J. W., Bailey G. W. and Gan H., *Appl. Clay Sci.*, 10, 417, 1996.

37. Kostka J. E., Haefele E., Viehweger R. and Stucki J. W., *Environ. Sci. Technol.*, 33, 3127, 1999.

38. Komadel P., Madejova J. and Stucki J. W., *Appl. Clay Sci.*, 34, 88, 2006.

Chapter 3
Synthesis and Characterization of Nanoclays

3.1. Introduction

Nanoclays have attracted substantial attention both in fundamental research and industrial applications because of their superior reinforcement properties in polymer nanocomposites; rheological modifier in paints and inks; sorbent for toxic pollutants from wastewater [1-8]. The applications of nanoclays in these fields mainly depend on the type of organic modifier used for the synthesis of nanoclays [9-11]. Most of the commercially available nanoclays are produced by exchange of alkali or alkali earth cations in the interlayer space of MMT with quaternary alkyl ammonium salts [12-14]. Other cations, such as phosphonium, imidazolium, pyridinium and imminium have also been used due to their higher thermal stability [15-16].

Several methods have been reported to synthesize clay/polymer nanocomposites; however, three methods (in situ polymerization, intercalation in solutions and melt processing) developed during the early stages of this field are widely applied [17-20]. The melt processing technique is mostly used because this process played an important role in speeding up the progress of the commercial production of clay/polymer nanocomposites [21]. Alkyl ammonium modified clays are thermally not very stable above 250 °C and start to degrade at nanocomposites processing temperature (200-300 °C). Therefore, organoclays prepared using quaternary alkyl ammonium salts are less suitable for most engineering plastics with high processing temperature [22-26]. The thermal stability of organoclays can be improved by intercalating quaternary phosphonium salts.

The first part of this chapter reports the synthesis of nanoclays using quaternary ammonium salts by the ion exchange interaction of quaternary ammonium salts with MMT of Indian origin. The effect of reaction temperature, concentration of MMT, different types of ammonium salts on the physico-chemical properties of nanoclays are studied in detail. The second part deals with the synthesis and characterization of nanoclays based on phosphonium salts. The emphasis is put on the thermal stability of the nanoclays derived from MMT and phosphonium salts.

3.2. Experimental Section

3.2.1. Materials

The raw bentonite lumps were collected from Barmer district (RB), Rajasthan. Ammonium and phosphonium salts used in this study (listed in Table 3.1) were purchased from Sigma-Aldrich, USA except dimethyldihydrogenatedtallowammonium chloride which was obtained from Cutch oil Ltd., India.

3.2.2. Synthesis of Nanoclay Using Ammonium Salts

The raw bentonite was purified by sedimentation technique [27] as discussed in chapter 2 and the purified fraction was designated as MMT through out this chapter. The synthesis of nanoclays under different reaction conditions using quaternary ammonium salts is tabulated in Table 3.2. The organoclays were prepared at different reaction temperature ranges, 25-30, 50-60 and 80-90 C with continuous stirring by adding 0.9 meq of 0.01M dimethyldihydrogenatedtallowammonium chloride (HT) solution in distilled water for 1 h. The clay slurry of different concentration (0.5, 1.0 and 1.5 per cent w/w) were made, ion exchanged by 0.01M HT (0.9 meq) at 80-90 C with stirring. The organoclays with different types of organic modifier are synthesized using 0.9 meq of strearyldimethyl-

Table 3.1. Ammonium and phosphonium salts used for preparation of nanoclays.

Name of Compounds	Molecular Formula
Ammonium salts	
Tetrabutylammonium chloride	$(C_4H_9)_4$ N (Cl)
Cetyltrimethylammonium bromide	$CH_3 (CH_2)_{15}$ N (Br) $(CH_3)_3$
Strearyldimethylbenzylammonium chloride	$C_6H_5 CH_2 (CH_2)_{17}$ N (Cl) $(CH_3)_2$
*Dimethyldihydrogenatedtallowammonium chloride	$(HT)_2$ N (Cl) $(CH_3)_2$
Phosphonium salts	
Tetrabutylphosphonium bromide	$(C_4H_9)_4$ P (Br)
Tributylhexadecylphosphonium bromide	$CH_3 (CH_2)_{15}$ P (Br) $(C_4H_9)_3$
Tributyltetradecylphosphonium chloride	$CH_3 (CH_2)_{13}$ P (Br) $(C_4H_9)_3$
Tetraphenylphosphonium bromide	$(C_6H_5)_4$ P (Br)
Methyltriphenylphosphonium bromide	CH_3 P (Br) $(C_6H_5)_3$
Ethyltriphenylphosphonium bromide	C_2H_5 P (Br) $(C_6H_5)_3$
Propyltriphenylphosphonium bromide	C_3H_7 P (Br) $(C_6H_5)_3$

*hydrogenatedtallow = ~ 65 per cent C18; ~ 30 per cent C16; ~ 5 per cent C14.

benzylammonium chloride (SMB), cetyltrimethylammonium bromide (CTAB) and (tetrabutylammonium chloride) TBA (0.01M solution), were added into MMT slurry (10 g MMT in 1 L distilled water) at 80-90 C with continuous stirring. The organoclays with different concentration of organic modifier were prepared by reacting MMT slurry (10 g MMT in 1 L distilled water) with 0.22, 0.43, 0.64 meq of SMB at 80-90 C with continuous stirring. Organoclays synthesized under different reaction parameters were filtered, washed with deionized water till free from halide ion (tested by 0.01M $AgNO_3$ solution), dried at 35 °C followed by overnight drying at 110 °C and then pulverized to pass through 300 mesh sieve and designated by OC 1, OC 2, OC 3, OC 4, OC 5, OC 6, OC 7, OC 8, OC 9, OC 10, OC 11 and OC 12 respectively as shown in Table 3.2.

3.2.3. Synthesis of Nanoclay Using Phosphonium Salts

10 g of MMT was dispersed in 1 L of distilled water. To this dispersion, 0.9 meq of phosphonium salts (as 0.01 M solution) was slowly added under continuous stirring at 80 °C within 1 h. The products were washed free from halide ions as tested using $AgNO_3$ solution, dried at 35 °C

followed by overnight drying at 110 °C and then pulverized to pass through 300 mesh sieve. The phosphonium-MMT was designated as P1 (tetrabutylphosphonium-MMT), P2 (hexadecyltributylphosphonium-MMT), P3 (tetradecyltributylphosphonium-MMT), P4 (tetraphenyl-phosphonium-MMT), P5 (methyltriphenylphosphonium-MMT), P6 (ethyltriphenylphosphonium-MMT) and P7 (propyltriphenyl-phosphonium-MMT).

3.2.4. Characterization

Powder X-ray diffraction (XRD) analysis was carried out with a Phillips powder diffractometer X' Pert MPD using PW3123/00 curved Cu-filtered Cu-Ká radiation with slow scan of 0.3°/s. Fourier transform infrared spectra (FTIR) were measured with the Perkin-Elmer-Spectrum GX Spectrophotometer as KBr pellet. The nanoclays were characterized by thermogravimetric analysis (Mettler-Toledo, TGA/SDTA 851e) by heating samples at 10 °C/min heating rate in the air flow of 40 mL/min. The particle size analysis (as dry powder) was done on Malvern Instrument - Master sizer 2000 at feed rate of 50 per cent and air pressure of 1 bar.

3.3. Results and Discussion (Quaternary Ammonium Based Nanoclays)

3.3.1. Effect of Reaction Parameters on Properties of Nanoclays

We have studied the effect of reaction parameters such as reaction temperature, concentration of clay, different types of organic modifier and concentration of organic modifier on properties of nanoclays. The physico-chemical properties of nanoclays vary with reaction parameters.

3.3.1.1. Effect of Reaction Temperature

The organoclays prepared under three different temperature ranges, 25-30 (OC 1), 50-60 (OC 2) and 80-90 C (OC 3) as shown in Table 3.2. The reaction temperature markedly affects the particle size and brightness of the nanoclay. Nanoclays are synthesized at 25-30 C (OC 1) and 50-60 C (OC 2). Average particle size of 8.2 and 7.9 µm, with 90 per cent of nanoclays in the particle size range of less than 20.2 and 16.8 µm respectively was obtained. The finer particle size with an average particle size of 3.6 and 90 per cent less than 12.3 µm is observed in OC 3, which is synthesized at 80-90 C reaction temperature. The finer particle size at

Table 3.2. Effect of reaction parameters on physico-chemical of nanoclay.

Effect of Reaction Parameters	Reaction Temperature		Conc. of Clay				Types of Organic Modifier			Conc. of Organic Modifier in Clay		
	OC 1	OC 2	OC 3	OC 4	OC 5	OC 6	OC 7	OC 8	OC 9	OC 10	OC 11	OC 12
Processing of nanoclays												
CEC of clay, meq/g	0.9	0.9	0.9	0.9	0.9	0.9	0.9	0.9	0.9	0.9	0.9	0.9
Clay content, per cent	1.0	1.0	1.0	0.5	1.0	1.5	1.0	1.0	1.0	1.0	1.0	1.0
Reaction Temp., C	25-30	50-60	80-90	80-90	80-90	80-90	80-90	80-90	80-90	80-90	80-90	80-90
*OM	#HT	#HT	#HT	#HT	#HT	#HT	1SMB	2CTAB	3TBA	1SMB	1SMB	1SMB
*OM, meq/g	0.9	0.9	0.9	0.9	0.9	0.9	0.9	0.9	0.9	0.22	0.43	0.64
Characterization of nanoclays												
Moisture cont., per cent	1.4	1.3	1.4	1.4	1.4	1.4	1.5	2.8	3.7	3.9	3.4	2.7
LOI, per cent	38.5	38.5	38.6	38.7	38.4	38.6	34.2	28.4	26.7	18.3	24.4	29.1
Brightness	72	79	86	86	86	82	83	78	65	66	73	79
Per cent C	30.7	30.7	30.7	30.7	30.7	30.7	22.3	14.6	4.4	5.6	11.2	16.8
Per cent H	4.8	4.7	4.7	4.7	4.6	4.7	3.8	2.8	1.4	1.0	1.8	2.9
Per cent N	0.9	1.0	0.9	1.0	0.9	0.9	0.8	0.9	0.6	0.3	0.5	0.6
d(0.1), μm	1.1	1.5	0.9	1.2	0.9	0.8	1.0	0.5	0.3	0.4	0.8	0.8
d(0.5), μm	8.2	7.9	3.6	3.8	3.6	4.1	3.7	9.3	13.6	14.2	13.8	10.3
d(0.9), μm	20.2	16.8	12.3	11.4	12.3	13.8	15.7	24.6	35.8	31.3	28.7	25.3
d-spacing, nm	3.5	3.5	3.5	3.4	3.5	3.5	2.6	1.9	1.4	1.5	1.6	1.9

*OM: Organic modifier; #HT: Dimethyldihydrogenated allow ammonium chloride; 1SMB: Stearyl dimethylbenzyl ammonium chloride; 2CTAB: Cetyltrimethyl ammonium bromide; 3TBA: Tetrabutylammonium chloride.

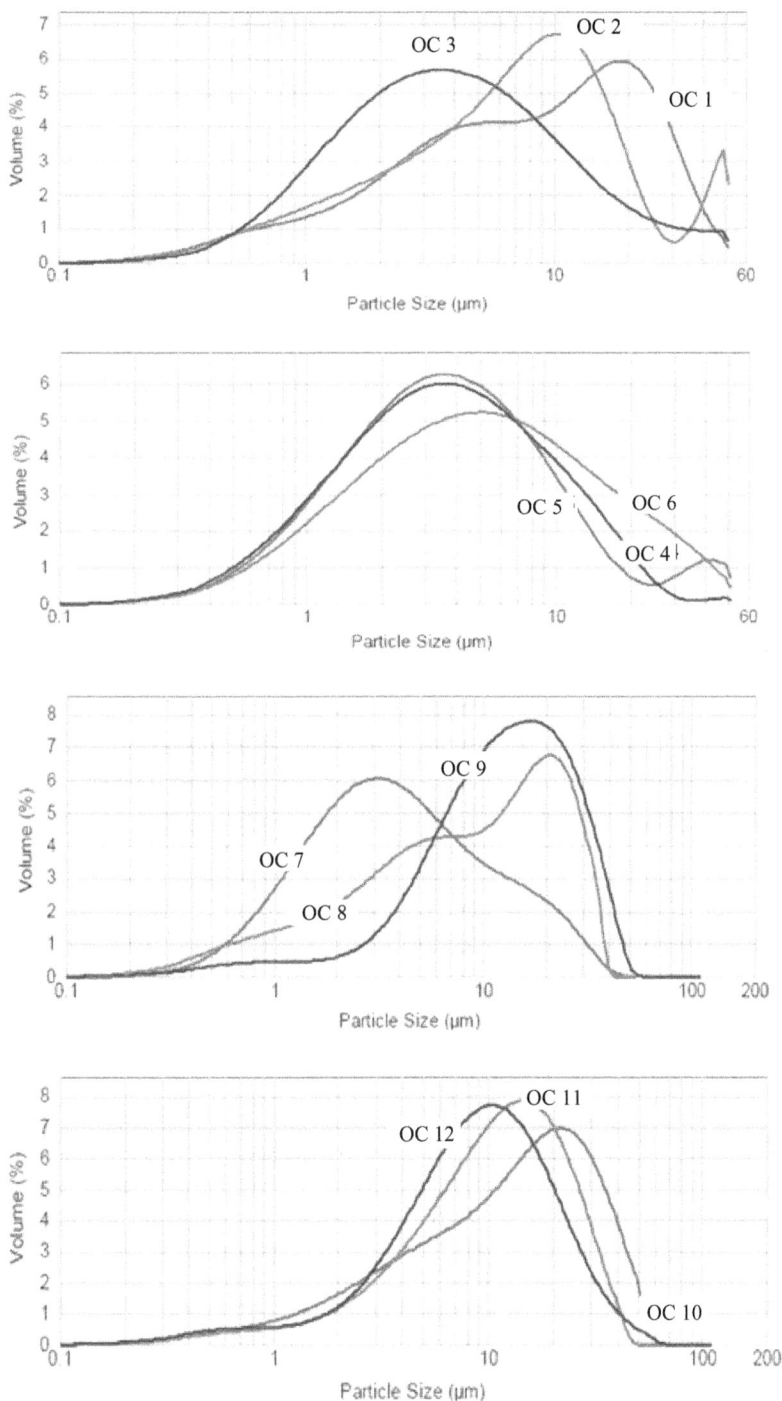

Figure 3.1. Particle size distribution patterns of organoclays synthesized under different reaction parameters.

higher temperature is due to better dispersion of MMT during synthesis of nanoclays. The particle size distribution patterns of nanoclays synthesized under variable reaction conditions are shown in Figure 3.1. The brightness of OC 1, OC 2 and OC 3 are 72, 79 and 86 respectively. The improvement in brightness is resulted because of particle size of nanoclays decreases as we go from lower to higher reaction temperature. The other properties like percentage of carbon, hydrogen and nitrogen, basal spacing are remain same in all three samples (OC 1 - OC 3).

3.3.1.2. Effect of Clay Concentration

The particle size and brightness of nanoclays (OC 4, OC 5 and OC 6) is also affected by the concentration of clay slurry during the preparation of nanoclay. The brightness of nanoclay (OC 6) synthesized at higher concentration (1.5 per cent w/w) is 82 with an average particle size of 4.1 µm. The optimum condition of concentration of clay for best brightness and finer particle size is 1 per cent w/w. Other properties of nanoclays are not affected by concentration of clay for synthesis of nanoclays.

3.3.1.3. Effect of Organic Modifier

The effect of organic modifier on the molecular packing with respect to alkyl chain length and surface area of intercalated organic cations within the interlayer space of MMT have been extensively studied [28-30]. Effect of organic modifier on properties of organoclays was studied by intercalating different quaternary ammonium salts, in which one or two of the four functional groups attached to nitrogen atom had varying alkyl chain length. The molecular surface areas and alkyl chain length (Connolly surface) determined using molecular modeling software at minimized energy (Accelrys, MS Modeling 3.2), also show dependence of particle size on surface area and chain length of quaternary ammonium cations (Figure 3.2) with higher surface area and longer alkyl chain length of quaternary ammonium cation resulting into finer particle size. The hydrophobicity, brightness, particle size and basal spacing are varying with types of organic modifier such as HT (OC 3), SMB (OC 7), CTAB (OC 8) and TBA (OC 9) as shown in Table 3.2. OC 3, wherein two long alkyl chain carrying ammonium ions intercalated MMT resulted in to finer particle size with an average particle size of 3.6 µm, improved brightness (86), higher basal spacing (3.5 nm) as discussed earlier also, is due to

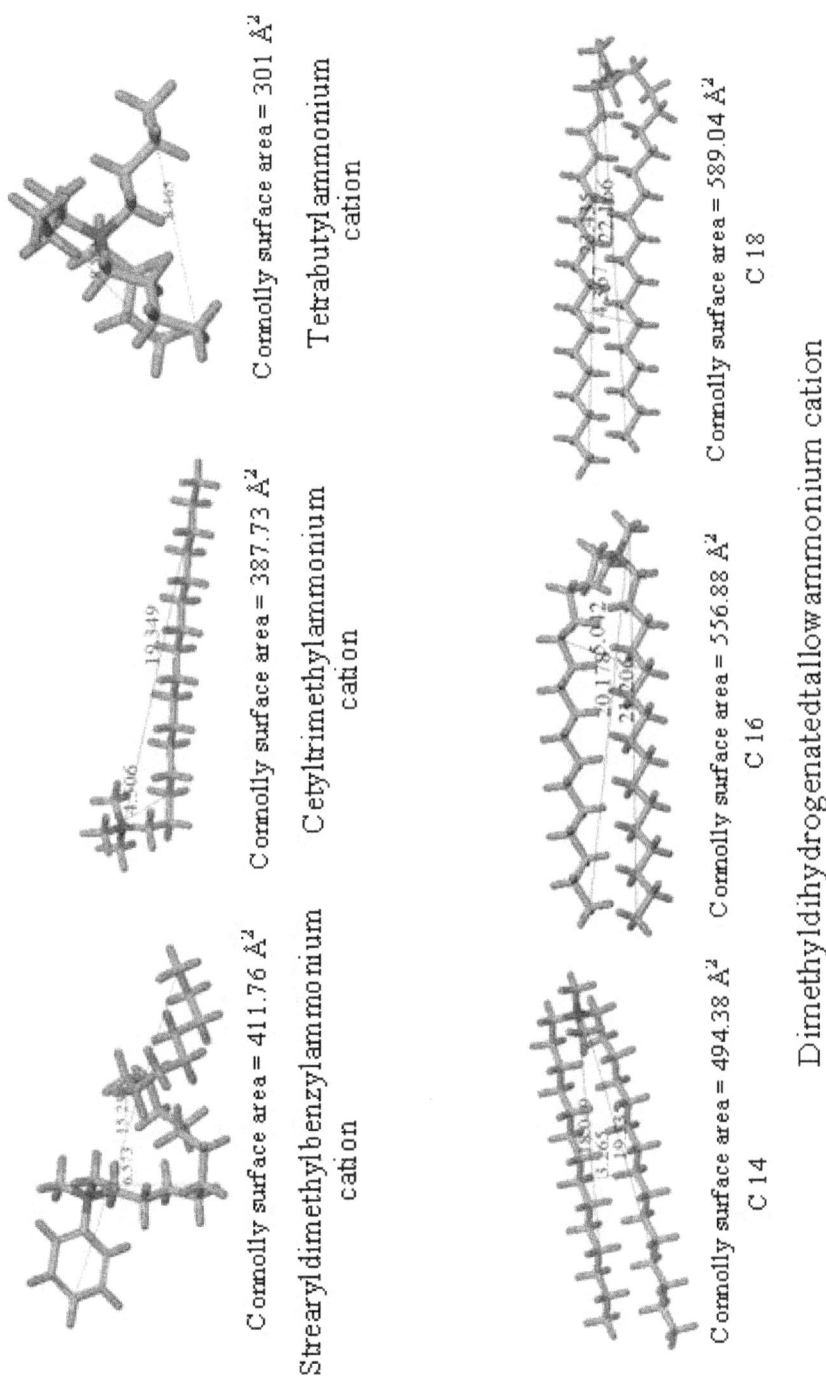

Tetrabutyl ammonium cation — Connolly surface area = 301 Å²

Cetyltrimethylammonium cation — Connolly surface area = 387.73 Å²

Strearyldimethylbenzylammonium cation — Connolly surface area = 411.76 Å²

C 18 — Connolly surface area = 589.04 Å²

C 16 — Connolly surface area = 556.88 Å²

C 14 — Connolly surface area = 494.38 Å²

Dimethyldihydrogenatedtallowammonium cation

Figure 3.2. Optimized energy structures of quaternary ammonium cations (Molecular modeling software; Accelreys, MS Modeling 3.2).

complete covering of silicate platelets which on during drying does not allowed agglomeration. The average particle size of OC 7, OC 8 and OC 9 are 3.7, 9.3 and 13.6 µm respectively. The brightness of OC 7, OC 8 and OC 9 are 83, 78 and 65, and basal spacing are 2.6, 1.9 and 1.4 nm respectively as shown in Figure 3.3.

3.3.1.4. Effect of Concentration of Organic Modifier

The nanoclays are synthesized by intercalation of SMB with varying CEC of 25 per cent (OC 10), 50 per cent (OC 11), 75 per cent (OC 12) and 100 per cent (OC 7) to study the effect of concentration of organic modifier on properties of nanoclays. The basal spacing of OC 10, OC 11, OC 12 and OC 7 are 1.5, 1.6, 1.9 and 2.6 nm respectively as shown in Figure 3.4, which indicates that the increase in amount of intercalation resulted into higher interlayer spacing. In other word, we can say as the number of carbon atom increases basal spacing also increases. The average particle size of OC 10, OC 11, OC 12 and OC 7 is 14.2, 13.8, 10.3 and 3.7 µm respectively as shown in Table 3.2. Again, the higher particle size is due to insufficient covering of silicate platelets. The hydrophobicity increases as the concentration of organic modifier in to interlayer spacing of nanoclays increases which is observed from moisture content of nanoclays as shown in Table 3.2. The percentage of carbon, hydrogen and nitrogen are varying with the amount of SMB inserted into MMT.

3.3.1.5. Thermal Stability of Nanoclays Based on ammonium Salts

Thermal stability of nanoclays is an important property for the application of nanoclays in melt compounding of engineering polymers and for high temperature resistant greases. The thermogravimetric analysis of RP (MMT), OC 3 (HT-MMT), OC 7 (SMB-MMT), OC 8 (CTAB-MMT) and OC 9 (TBA-MMT) are shown in Figure 3.5. The initial weight loss up to 150 °C is due to elimination of moisture in RP and OC 9. As the organic content in OC 3, OC 7 and OC 8 is higher as compare to OC 9, these are hydrophobic and show only 1-1.5 per cent wt loss in this temperature range. The degradation of organic modifier attached to MMT surface is started at 170, 190, 220 and 250 °C for OC 9, OC 8 OC 3 and OC 7, respectively. It is clear from this observation that the organic modifier with shorter alkyl chain started to degrade faster than organic modifier with longer alkyl chain. As shown in Figure 3.5, the highest thermal stability

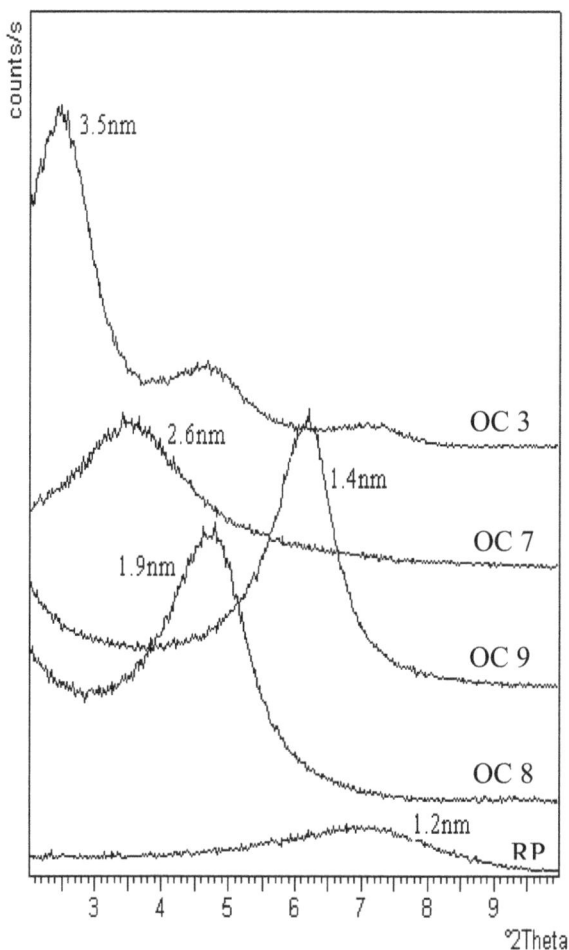

Figure 3.3. PXRD pattern shows effect of different types of organic modifier on basal spacing of nanoclays.

is observed for OC 7 due to presence of aromatic functional group in addition to longer alkyl chain. The organic modifiers are degraded within temperature range of 170-450 °C. The weight loss in the temperature region 500-700 °C is due to loss of covalently bound hydroxyl group at the edges of the alumino-silicate platelets.

3.4. Results and Discussions (Phosphonium Based Nanoclays)

3.4.1. FTIR Study of Phosphonium Based Nanoclays

The characterizations of MMT and organically modified MMT using FTIR have been extensively reported [31-34]. In the FTIR spectra of the

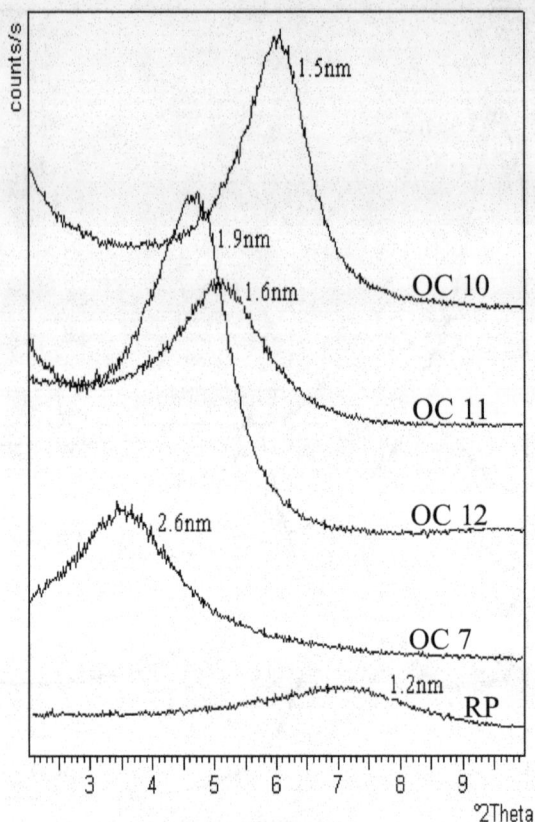

Figure 3.4. PXRD pattern shows effect of concentration organic modifier on basal spacing of nanoclays.

purified bentonite (Figure 3.6), the bands between 3500 and 3700 cm^{-1} and near 3400 cm^{-1} are indicative of MMT. The broad band centered near 3400 cm^{-1} is due to –OH stretching mode of interlayer water. The bands at 3620 and 3698 cm^{-1} are due to –OH stretching mode of Al–OH and Si–OH of MMT structure. The bands at 3698 cm^{-1} due to –OH stretching vibration may also be due to the presence of small quantity of kaolinite. The shoulders and the broadness of the –OH bands are mainly due to contributions of several structural –OH groups occurring in this smectite. The overlaid absorption peaks in the region of 1640 cm^{-1} is attributed to –OH bending mode of adsorbed water. The characteristic peak at 1115 cm^{-1} is due to Si–O stretching, out-of-plane Si–O stretching mode for MMT. The band at 1035 cm^{-1} is attributed to Si–O stretching (inplane) vibration for layered silicates.

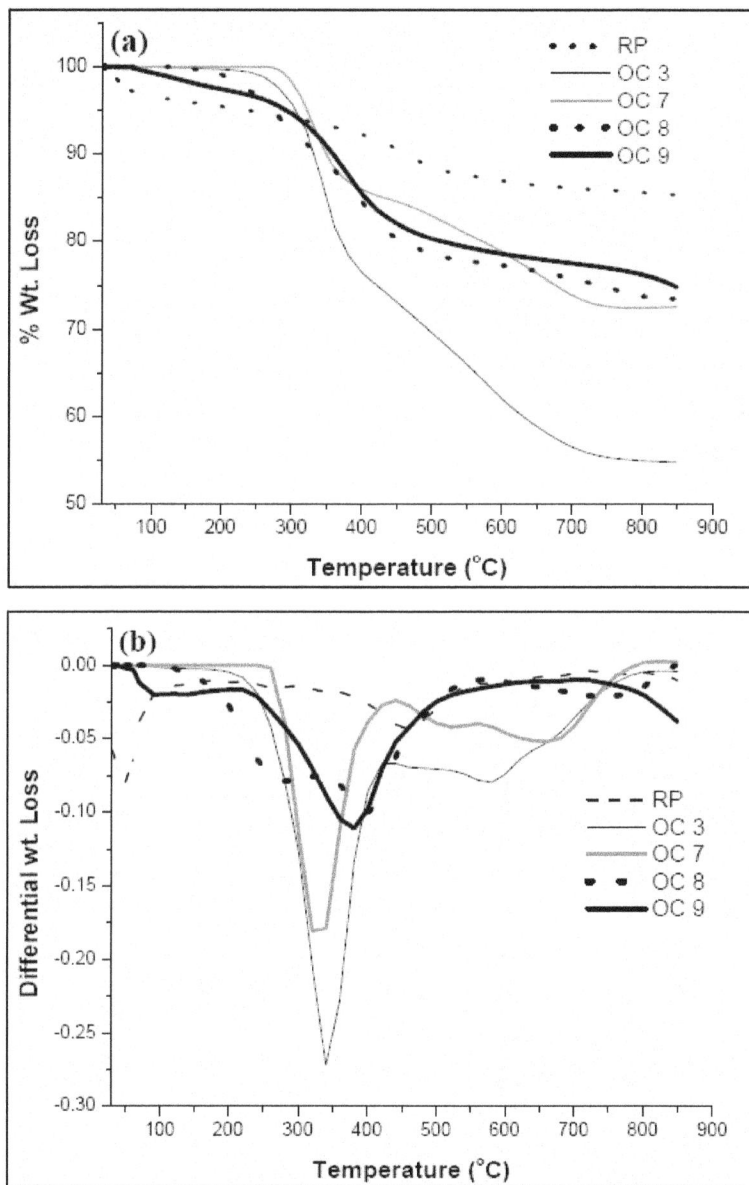

Figure 3.5. (a) TGA and **(b)** DTA curves for nanoclays with different quaternary ammonium cations (OC 3, 7, 8 and 9) and MMT (RP).

The IR peaks at 915, 875 and 836 cm^{-1} are attributed to AlAlOH, AlFeOH and AlMgOH bending vibration. In the FTIR spectra of P1, P2 and P3, the peaks at 2940 and 2850 cm^{-1} are ascribed to the asymmetric

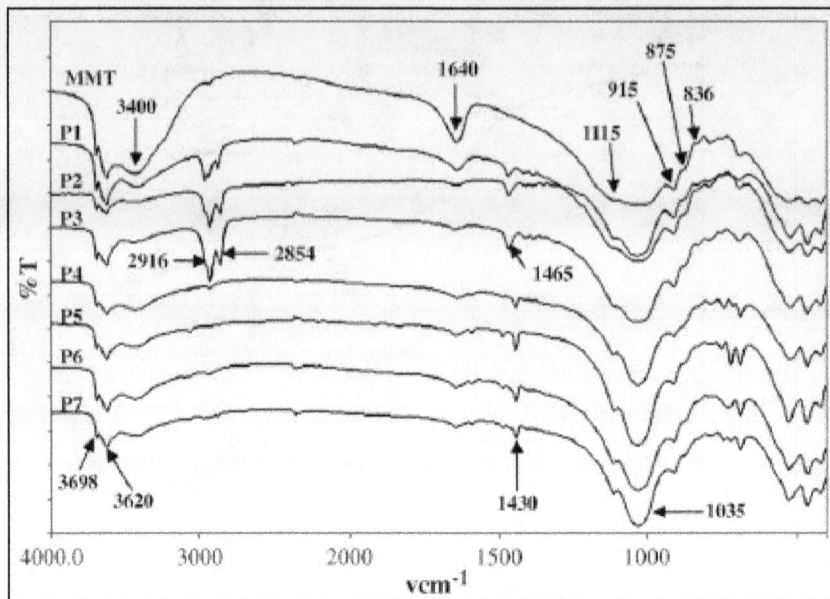

Figure 3.6. FTIR spectra of MMT and phosphonium-MMT (P1, P2, P3, P4, P5, P6 and P7).

and symmetric vibration of methylene groups $(CH2)_n$ of the aliphatic chain. Tetrabutylphosphonium-MMT (P1) shows a weak intensity of the –OH bending vibration at 1640 cm^{-1} due to adsorbed water. The phenyl ring attached to the phosphonium atom displayed an unusually sharp and relatively strong vibration band at 1430 cm^{-1} as shown in the infrared spectrum of P4, P5, P6 and P7. In addition to this, there is also the HCH stretching vibration band at 1465 cm^{-1} in IR spectrum of all phosphonium-MMT except tetraphenyl-phosphonium-MMT (P4). The IR absorption bands in the low frequency region of the upgraded bentonite and the phosphonium MMT analogues

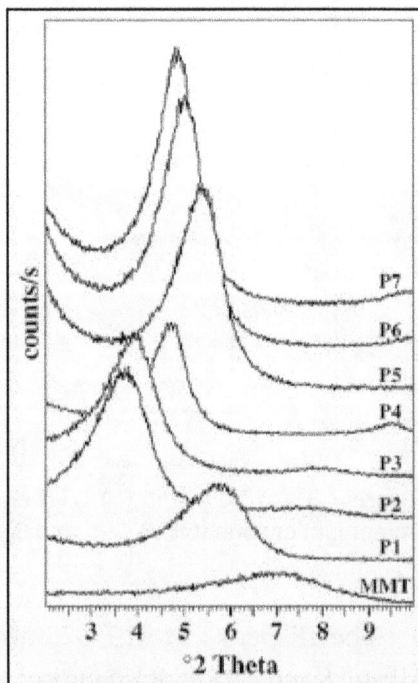

Figure 3.7. PXRD pattern of MMT and phosphonium-MMTs.

were largely comparable indicating that the MMT has not changed upon exchange of the interlayer sodium/calcium ions by the phosphonium cations.

3.4.2. PXRD Study of Phosphonium Based Nanoclays

The PXRD data show that basal spacing increased with the alkyl chain length (Figure 3.7). For the MMT, the spacing was 1.21 nm while the basal spacing for the P1 is 1.4 nm, and for the P2 and P3, 2.32 and 2.19 nm. The basal spacing of the samples P4, P5, P6 and P7 was nearly the same (1.76 ± 0.065 nm) as the cations are of similar size. The molecular

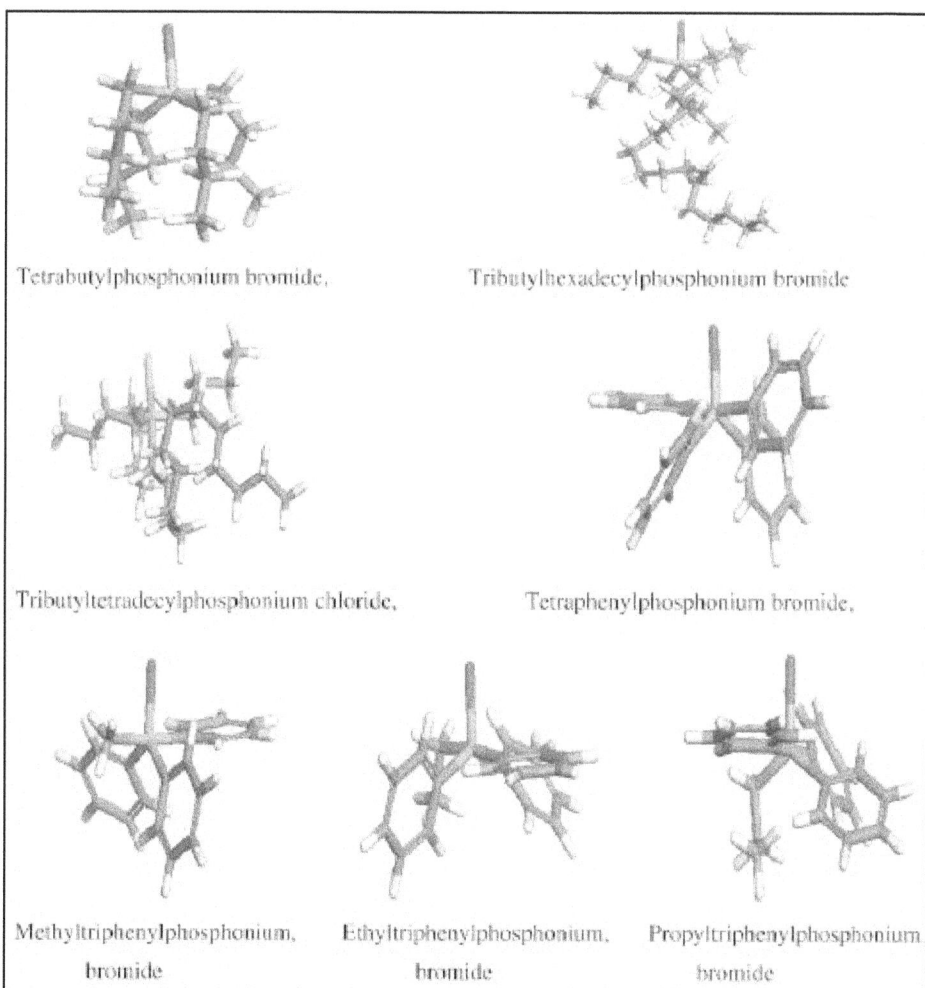

Tetrabutylphosphonium bromide,

Tributylhexadecylphosphonium bromide

Tributyltetradecylphosphonium chloride,

Tetraphenylphosphonium bromide,

Methyltriphenylphosphonium, bromide

Ethyltriphenylphosphonium, bromide

Propyltriphenylphosphonium bromide

Figure 3.8. Optimized energy structures of phosphonium salts (molecular modeling software; Accelreys, MS Modeling 3.2).

shape of the phosphonium cations were determined using molecular modeling software (Accelreys, MS Modeling 3.2) (Figure 3.8). It is expected that phosphonium cations will occupy configuration inside the interlayer space so that the positively charged phosphorous is closer to the negatively charged silicate layer to maximize electrostatic interaction.

The basal spacing values were plotted (Figure 3.9) against the maximum molecular length for all phosphonium cations with this configuration. The linear variation observed between the basal spacing and the molecular length do support the proposed configuration of phosphonium cations inside the interlayer space.

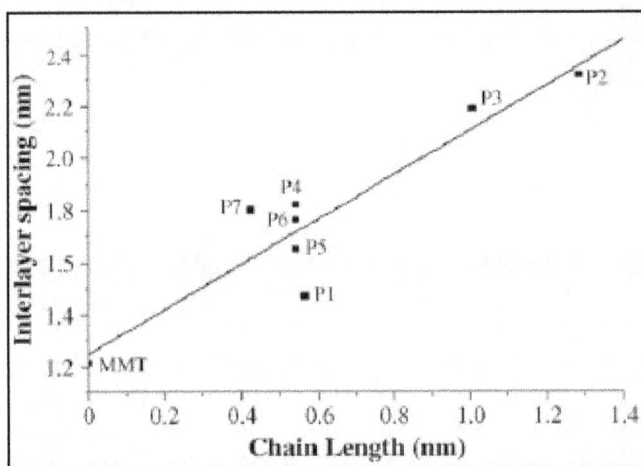

Figure 3.9. Correlation of basal spacing with chain length of organic moiety in phosphonium- MMT.

3.4.3. Particle Size Distribution of Phosphonium Based Nanoclays

The particle size distributions significantly depended on the alkyl chain length of phosphonium cations (Figure 3.10 and Table 3.3). P2 showed finer particle size as compared to P1 and P3. P4 showed a finer particle size distribution compared to P5, P6 and P7. These observations can be explained in terms of the aggregation of the montmorillonite particles in "house of cards" structure of clay observed in aqueous dispersion [35-40]. When MMT is dispersed in de-ionized water at slightly acidic conditions, positively charged edges are attracted to negatively charged surfaces of the platelets to form a three dimensional "house of cards" structure (Figure 3.11) which contains hundreds or thousands of silicate platelets.

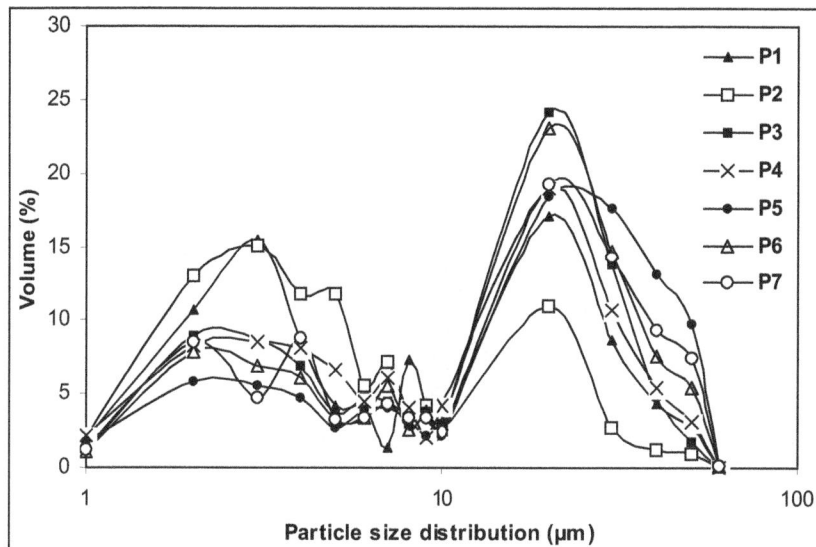

Figure 3.10. Particle size distributions of phosphonium-MMT (P1, P2, P3, P4, P5, P6 and P7).

Table 3.3. Particle size distribution of phosphonium-MMT (P1, P2, P3, P4, P5, P6 and P7) and molecular surface area of phosphonium salts.

Particle Size/ Organoclays	P1	P2	P3	P4	P5	P6	P7
d(0.1), μm	1.19	1.15	1.31	1.15	1.74	1.49	1.41
d(0.5), μm	5.40	3.88	8.32	6.75	14.72	10.30	10.15
d(0.9), μm	25.86	13.34	26.89	28.47	39.71	33.44	36.86
d(0.99), μm	46.71	39.35	43.52	46.91	51.00	49.94	50.66
Molecular surface area (Conolly surface) of phosphonium salts, $Å^2$/molecule							
$Å^2$/molecule	300.14	510.67	490.65	384.03	329.76	336.54	345.66

The particle size of clay in dispersion depends on the number of the platelets forming this structure. When alkyl/aryl phosphonium salts are added to aqueous dispersions, the positively charged phosphonium cations will also interact with negatively charged surface of the clay mineral and reduce its interactions with positively charged edges of other platelets and thereby decrease the number of platelets in the "house of cards" structure. Subsequent drying process will, therefore, yield finer particles. The alkyl phosphonium cations with longer carbon chains (hexadecyltributyl) are likely to cover the clay mineral surface more

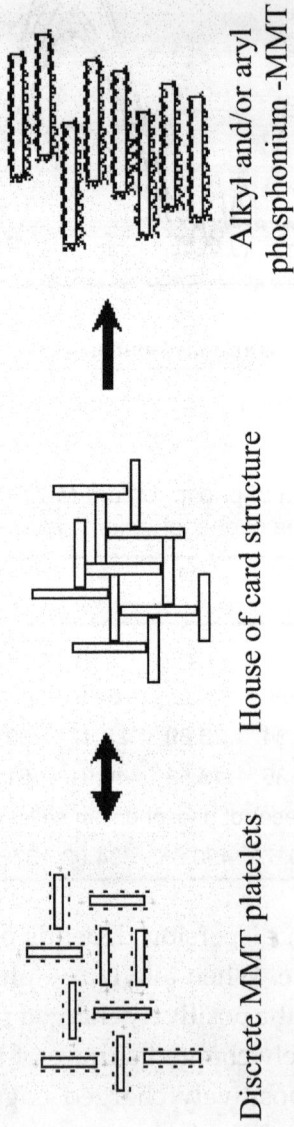

Figure 3.11. Formation of alkyl and/or aryl phosphonium-MMT from discrete platelets by breaking House of cards structure.

efficiently than phosphonium cations with smaller carbon chains (tetrabutyl or tetradecyltributyl) and lead, therefore, to finer particle. P4, P5, P6 and P7 have similar numbers of carbon atoms as P2 and P3; however,

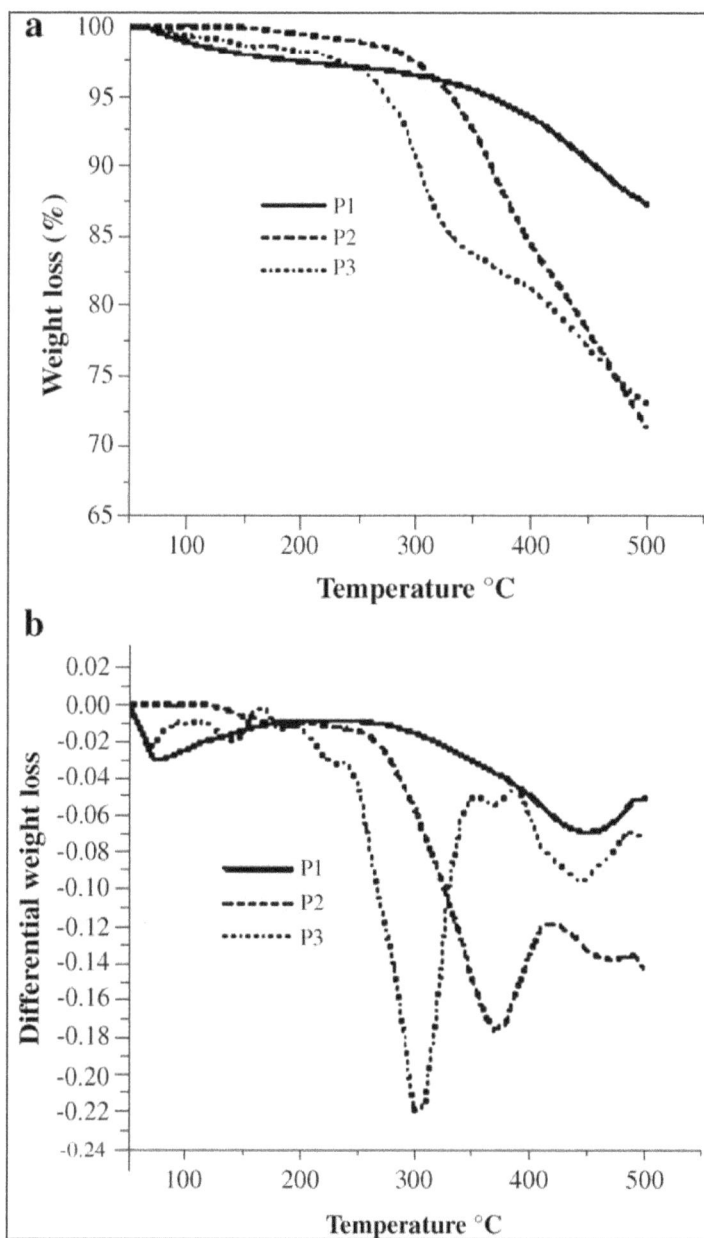

Figure 3.12. (a) Thermogravimetric analysis of P1, P2 and P3 up to 500 °C; (b) differential thermogravimetric analysis of P1, P2 and P3 up to 500 °C.

these show broader particle size distribution because of smaller organic moieties. The phosphonium- MMT with shorter alkyl chains or cyclic groups (tetraphenyl, methyl/ethyl/propyl triphenyl) will cover the surface

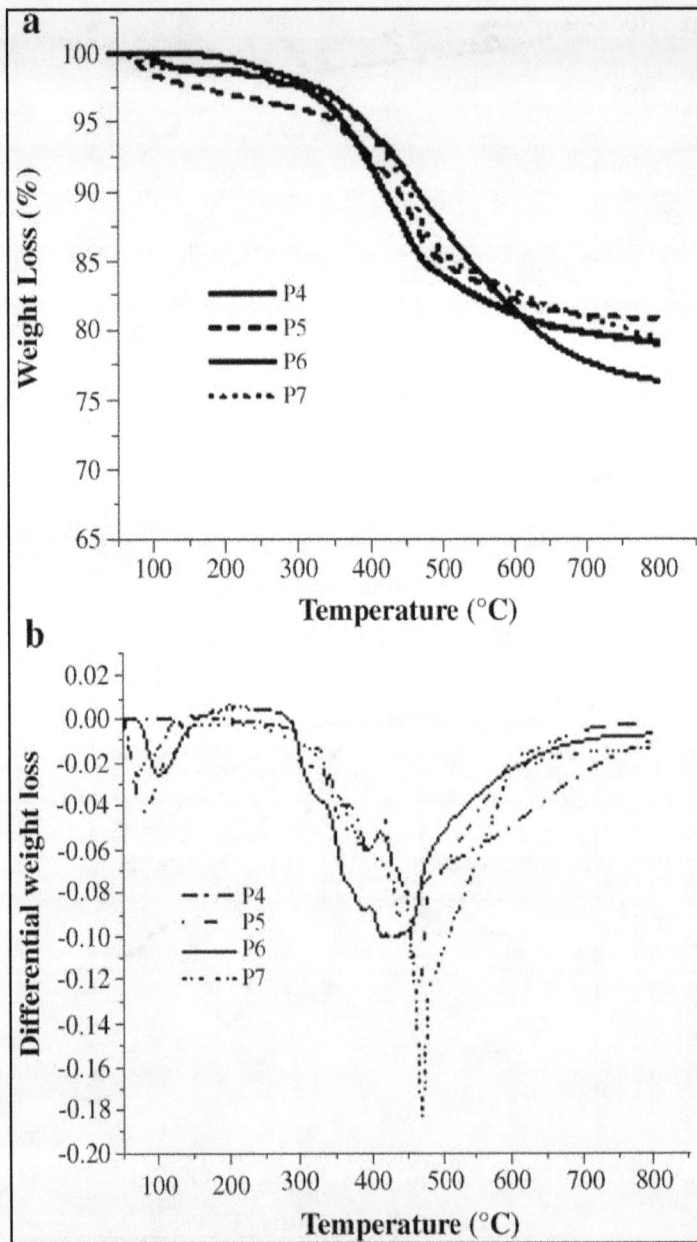

Figure 3.13. (a) Thermogravimetric analysis of P4, P5, P6 and P7 up to 800 °C; (b) differential thermogravimetric analysis of P4, P5, P6 and P7 up to 800 °C.

of a platelet to a smaller degree compared to the longer chain derivatives. As a result, organoclays prepared using aryl phosphonium salts will have a "house of cards" structure with a higher number of platelets that on drying results in a broader particle size distribution. The molecular surface areas (Conolly surface) determined using the molecular modeling software (Accelreys, MS Modeling 3.2), also reveal the dependence of the particle size distribution on the surface area of molecular cations (Table 3.3) showing finer particle size distribution for higher molecular surface areas except tetrabutylphosphonium-MMT.

3.4.4. Thermal Stability of Phosphonium Based Nanoclays

Comparison of the thermal stability of the three alkyl substituted phosphonium-MMT(P1, P2 and P3) and four aryl and/or alkyl substituted phosphonium MMT (P4, P5, P6 and P7) as shown in Figure 3.12 a, b and 3.13 a, b. The TGA data show improvement in thermal stability for all aryl and/or alkyl substituted phosphonium MMT as compared to only alkyl phosphonium-MMT. The tetraphenylphosphonium-MMT (P4) showed the highest thermal stability at 350–400 °C (5 per cent decomposition), while substitution of phenyl group by a methyl, ethyl or propyl group (P5, P6 and P7) led lower thermal stability of 300–350 °C (5 per cent decomposition). The alkyl chain length also affects the thermal stability. The thermal stability increases with the alkyl chain length. However, P1 having tetrabutylphosphonium as interlayer ion shows thermal stability up to 350 °C, almost equivalent tetraphenylphosphonium MMT. This is due to the high thermal stability of tetrabutylphosphonium cation.

References

1. Baskaralingam P., Pulikesi M., Elango D., Ramamurthi V. and Sivanesan S., *J. Hazard. Mater.*, 128, 138, 2006.

2. Lizhong Z., Baoliang C. and Xueyou S., *Environ. Sci. Technol.*, 34, 468, 2000.

3. Lin F. H., Leeb Y. H., Jianb C. H., Wonga J. M., Shieha M. J. and Wanga C. Y., *Biomaterials*, 23, 1981, 2002.

4. Kwak S. Y., Jeong Y. J., Park J. S. and Choy J. H., *Solid State Ionics*, 151, 229, 2002.

5. Patel H. A., Somani R. S., Bajaj H. C. and Jasra R. V., *Bull. Mater. Sci.*, 29(2), 133, 2006.

6. Manias E., Touny A., Wu L., Strawhecker K., Lu B. and Chung, T. C., *Chem. Mater.*, 13, 3516, 2001.

7. Ray S. S. and Okamoto M., *Prog. Polym. Sci.*, 28, 1539, 2003.

8. Manias E., *Presented at Additives 2003*, San Francisco, CA, April 2003.

9. Faiza B. and Lagaly G., *Appl. Clay Sci.*, 19, 1, 2001.

10. Maguy J., Jocelyne M. B., Luc D. and Ronan L., *Solid State Science*, 7, 610, 2005.

11. Theng B. K. G., 1979, Formation and Properties of Clay-Polymer Complexes, *Elsevier Scientific Publisher*, Amsterdam.

12. Grim, R.E; Guven, N., 1978, Bentonites-Geology, Mineralogy, Properties and Uses, *Elsevier Scientific Publisher*, Amsterdam.

13. Worrall, W. E., 1986, Clays and Ceramic Raw materials; 2nd ed., *Elsevier Scientific Publisher*, Amsterdam.

14. Olphen H. V., 1976, Clay Colloid Chemistry; For Clay Technologists, Geologists and Soil Scientists; 2nd ed., *John Wiley and Sons*, New York.

15. MeAtee J. L., *Amer. Min.*, 44, 1230, 1959.

16. Lagaly, G., *Clay Miner.*, 16, 1, 1981.

17. Deniss H. R., Hunter D. L. Chang D., Kim S., White J. L., Chow J. W. and Paul D. R., *Polymer*, 42, 9513, 2001.

18. Gao F., *Presented at Organic-Inorganic Hybrid II. PRA*, Guildford, 2002.

19. Garces J. M., Moll D. J., Bicerano J., Fibiger R. And McLeod D. G., *Adv. Mater.*, 12, 1835, 2000.

20. Hasegawa N., Kawasumi M., Kato M., Usuki A. and Okada, A., *J. Appl. Polym. Sci.*, 67, 87, 1998.

21. LeBaron P. C., Wang Z. and Pinnavaia T. J., *Appl. Clay Sci.*, 15, 11, 1999.

22. Wang D. and Wilkie C. A., *Polym. Degrad. Stabil.*, 82, 309, 2003.

23. Wei X., Zongming G., Kunlei L., Wei-Ping P., Vaia R., Doug H. and Singh A., *Thermoch. Acta*, 367–368, 339, 2001.

24. Wei X., Zongming G., Wei-Ping P., Doug H., Singh A., and Vaia R., *Chem. Mater.*, 13, 2979, 2001.

25. Wei R. X., Wei-Ping P., Doug H., Bryan K., Loon-Seng T. and Vaia R., Chem. Mater., 14, 4837, 2002.

26. Patel H. A., Somani R. S., Bajaj H. C. and Jasra R. V., *Appl. Clay Sci.*, 35, 194, 2006.

27. Patel H. A., Somani R. S., Bajaj H. C. and Jasra R. V., *Curr. Sci.*, 92(2), 1, 2006.

28. Vaia R. A., Teukolsky R. K. and Giannelis E. P., *Chem. Mater.*, 6, 1017, 1994.

29. Paul D. R., Zeng Q. H., Yu A. B. and Lu, G. Q., *J. Collo. Inter. Sci.*, 292, 462, 2005.

30. Meier L. P. Nueesch R. and Madsen F. T., *J. Collo. Inter. Sci.*, 238, 24, 2001.

31. Lee J.Y. and Lee H. K., *Mater. Chem. Phys.*, 85, 410, 2004.

32. Madejova J., *Vibrat. Spectro.*, 31, 1, 2003.

33. Tyagi B., Chudasama C. D. and Jasra R.V., *Spectroch. Acta Part A*, 64 (2), 273, 2006.

34. Xi Y., Ding Z., Hongping H. and Frosr R. L., *Spectro. Acta Part A*, 61, 515, 2005.

35. Lagaly G. and Ziesmer S., *Adv. Colloi. Inter.*, 100-102, 105, 2003.

36. Dijkstra M., Hansen J. P. and Madden P. A., *Phys. Rev. Lett.*, 75, 2236, 1995.

37. Tambach T. J., Bolhuis P. G., Hensen E. J. M. and Smit B., *Langmuir*, 22, 1223, 2006.

38. Penner D. and Lagaly G., *Appl. Clay Sci.*, 19, 131, 2001.

39. Fossum J. O., *Physica A*, 270, 270, 1999.

40. Janek, M. and Lagaly G., *Appl. Clay Sci.*, 19, 121, 2001.

Chapter 4
Polypropylene/Nanoclays Nanocomposites and Nanoclays for Paints

4.1. Introduction

In polymer/nanoclay nanocomposites (PNC), a few wt. per cent of each silicate layer of clay mineral is randomly and homogeneously dispersed on a molecular level in the polymer matrix. When molded, the mechanical, thermal and barrier properties of these materials are superior to those of pristine polymers and/or conventional composites. The effects are very striking, and have become well known since many excellent reviews have been published [1-10].

PNC was firstly invented at Toyota Central R&D Labs (Toyota) [11-12]. It bore a new concept of polymer nanocomposites, expanded the field of polymer science including preparation, structure and interfaces and led to new applications for automotive, electric and food industries. Passenger cars equipped with a PCN part were launched in 1989, only 4 years after this discovery. Since then, extensive worldwide research on PCN has been conducted not only in the industrial sector but also in the academic sector. At present, development has widened into almost every engineering polymer including polypropylene, polyethylene, polystyrene, polyvinylchloride, acrylonitrile butadiene styrene polymer, polymethylmethacrylate, polyethyleneterephthalate, ethylene-vinyl acetate copolymer, polyacrylonitrile, polycarbonate, polyethylene oxide, epoxy resin, polyimide, polylactide, polycaprolactone, phenolic resin, poly p-phenylene vinylene, polypyrrole, rubber, starch, polyurethane, and polyvinylpyridine [13-20].

The major use of polymers is in molded products. Polymers have been successfully reinforced using glass fiber, talc, calcium carbonate, carbon black and other inorganic fillers. The content of the filler is usually between 20 and 40 wt. per cent of a composite and sometimes exceeds 50 wt. per cent in thermosetting resins. Polymers and fillers are not homogeneously mixed on a microscopic level, and are composed of different phases. The interface is not large, and interaction between the polymer and the filler is limited [21-25].

Polypropylene (PP) is the most widely used polymer in the automotive industry and in commodity products. While it is less expensive, its mechanical and thermal properties are inferior to engineering plastics such as nylons. However, there is a strong need to improve the mechanical properties of PP, owing to its low price. After nylon 6 was successfully developed, various research efforts were made worldwide to reinforce PP using nanoclay, but to the best of our knowledge no successful examples of reinforced PNC have yet been reported. Since natural pristine clay is hydrophilic and PP is hydrophobic, there is enormous difficulty in making PNC. Many studies have been focused on PP and nanoclay based PNC because of the cost effectiveness of PNC in the automotive, packaging and appliance industries. Currently, there are three different main approaches to the preparation of PP based PNC: the solution process [26], in-situ polymerization [27], and melt compounding [28]. In fact, melt compounding has proved to be an excellent technique because of its ease, versatility and benign character, with respect to the environment. However, uniform dispersion of nanoclay in the polymer matrix is essential to achieve the improvements in the thermo-mechanical properties. The nanoclays have a strong tendency to agglomerate because of the natural incompatibility between the hydrophilic MMT nanoparticles and the hydrophobic PP matrix. These aggregates are very difficult to break down by the limited shear force during melt compounding. To break down nanoparticle agglomerates and produce nanostructure composites, many specific approaches have been attempted in recent years. These approaches can be mainly summarized as: (i) modification of the MMT surface by surfactant [29] or (ii) modification of the PP matrix by incorporating a more hydrophilic compatibilizer [30], or (iii) modification of processing conditions [31].

Various efforts have been made to improve the clay dispersion and PNC properties. Ton-That *et al.*, [30] utilized maleic-anhydride-grafted PP (MA-g-PP), with varying molecular weight and acid content, to enhance the interaction with the organoclay. Manias *et al.*, [32] used two approaches, either by using functionalized PP and common organoclay or by using neat PP and a semi-fluorinated organoclay; to improve the dispersion and the ultimate properties of PP based PNC. Utracki *et al.*, [33] used an extensional flow mixer combined with twin screw extruder or single screw extruder to improve the dispersion of organoclay-PP matrix. However, up to now, full exfoliation of nanoclay in PP by melt compounding has remained difficult to achieve [34]; in most cases, the clay in the PP matrix is still in the form of multilayered stacks, with expanded galleries, rather than individual clay platelets. In principle, the PNC formation is thermodynamically driven; therefore, this process can spontaneously happen only with the reduction of free energy during mixing. Consequently, the formation of PNC is dependent on the interaction between the entropy and enthalpy factors. Obviously, the conformational entropy of the polymer chains decreases when they are forced to be confined inside the organoclay interlayer. To balance the penalty originating from the polymer chains confinement, it is crucial to form an initial organoclay structure, to be able to significantly increase its dispersion in the polymer matrix, thus increasing the entropy of the system. This could be achieved by a larger initial gallery gap resulting from the intercalant with longer aliphatic tails and high intercalant coverage on the MMT surface. However, high intercalant coverage is not always better, because the reactive sites on the clay surface could be hindered. Therefore, intercalant should not be too crowded on the MMT surface if there is good interaction between the compatibilizer and the MMT.

Nanoclay prepared from Indian bentonite and imported nanoclay are compounded with PP and MA-g-PP in twin screw extruder in this part of the chapter. The compounded PNCs are molded by injection molding into a standard specimen for studying its tensile, flexural and impact strength. The imported and indigenous nanoclays are fully characterized and are further used for the synthesis of PNCs.

4.2. Experimental Section

4.2.1. Materials

Polypropylene (PP) copolymers used for this study was obtained from Reliance Industries under the trade name AMI 400N. The compatibilizers used are maleic anhydride functionalized PP (MA-g-PP) obtained from Compton Chemicals Company. Imported nanoclay (Cloisite 20A) is purchased from Southern Clay Products, Inc., USA. Dioctadecyldimethylammonium chloride (DADO), $[CH_3(CH_2)_{17}]_2$ $N(CH_3)Cl$ was purchased from Sigma-Aldrich. Montmorillonite (MMT) is obtained by purifying Indian bentonite as discussed in previous chapters. The properties of PP, MA-g-PP and Cloisite 20A are given below,

Properties of Polypropylene (PP)

Polypropylene (PP) copolymers; **AMI 400N**

☆ Density: 0.905 gm/cc

☆ Melt index (ASTM D 1238): 230°C/2.16 kg - 40 gm/10min

☆ Vicat Softening Point (ASTM D 1525): 150 ° C

☆ Manufacturer: Reliance Industries Ltd.

Properties of Compatibilizer

Maleic anhydride grafted polypropylene (MA-g-PP); **Polybond 3200**

☆ MFI (190/2.16): 115 g/10 min.

☆ Density at 23°C: 0.91 g/cc

☆ Maleic Anhydride Level: 1.0 wt per cent

☆ Manufacturer: Crompton Chemicals Company.

Imported Nanoclay (Cloisite 20A)

The Cloisite 20A is prepared from Cloisite Na (MMT) and dimethyldihydrogenatedtallow ammonium chloride (DMDAC). The structure of DMDAC is,

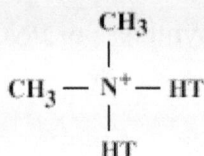

$$CH_3 - \overset{\displaystyle CH_3}{\underset{\displaystyle HT}{\overset{\displaystyle |}{\underset{\displaystyle |}{N^+}}}} - HT$$

Where HT is hydrogenated Tallow (~65 per cent C18; ~30 per cent C16; ~5 per cent C14).

4.2.2. Synthesis of Nanoclay

The nanoclay was synthesized by exchanging 90 meq of exchangeable cation per 100 g of MMT. 1 per cent solution of dioctadecyl-dimethylammonium chloride (5.4 g) were added within 45 min at 80 C under vigorous stirring to beaker contained 10.2 g of MMT dispersed in 1 L of distilled water. Organoclay synthesized was filtered, washed with hot distilled water till free from halide ion as tested by 0.01M $AgNO_3$ solution, dried at 60 C for 24 h. The dried organoclay was ground and passed through 300 mesh sized sieves. Sample obtained was designated as DODA 90.

4.2.3. Compounding on Twin Screw Extruder

PP/nanoclay nanocomposites were prepared using two nanoclay samples (Cloisite 20A and DODA 90) on twin screw extruder. Nanocomposites were prepared at 4.5 g scale using *DSM Micro 5* twin-screw extruder and were characterized for structure and mechanical properties. The compounding was performed at screw speed of 100 rpm at temperature of 200 °C for 5-7 min., simultaneously the compounded PNCs were molded in *DSM injection molding machine* to obtained standard specimen for further study. The PP and PP with polybond 3200 were also processed under identical conditions for comparison with PNCs. The amount of PP, nanoclays and polybond 3200 are given in Table 4.1. Films of PP, PPB, PNC 1 and PNC 2 were prepared using pellets obtained from extruder by hot pressing ~1 g of pellets at 200 °C temperature and 6 metric ton of pressure for 3 min on hot pressing machine followed by controlled cooling with water. These films were then used for wide angle X-ray diffraction (WAXD).

Table 4.1. Composition of PP, Nanoclay and polybond 3200 in PNCs compounded on twin screw extruder (*Batch scale 4.5 g*).

Sample Ids	Polymer Grade	Nanoclays		Compatibilizer
	AMI 400N	Cloisite 20 A	DODA 90	Polybond 3200
PP	100 per cent	–	–	–
PPB	95 per cent	–	–	5 per cent
PNC 1	90 per cent	5 per cent	–	5 per cent
PNC 2	90 per cent	–	5 per cent	5 per cent

4.2.4. Characterizations

Fourier transform infrared spectra (FTIR) were measured with the Perkin-Elmer-Spectrum GX Spectrophotometer as KBr pellet. The particle size analysis (as dry powder) was done on Malvern Instrument - Master sizer 2000 at feed rate of 50 per cent and air pressure of 1 bar. The intercalation of the polymer in nanoclay layers was confirmed using WAXD. WAXD has been employed to determine the changes in d-spacing of nanoclays and PCNs. Measurements were carried out with a Phillips powder diffractometer X' Pert MPD using PW3123/00 curved Cu-filtered Cu-Ká having wavelength of 0.01 nm radiation with slow scan of 0.3°/s in the 2θ ranges from 2 to 10 DSC studies were carried out using a Mettler-Toledo over a temperature range of 50-200 ℃. A controlled heating rate and cooling rate was maintained at 10 ℃/min. The tests were carried out in inert nitrogen atmosphere. The melting point (T_m), crystallization temperature (T_c) and per cent crystallinity of PP, PPB and PNCs were determined using DSC heating and cooling scans. The tensile testing of injection molded specimen was performed on Instron Universal testing Machine model 4204, Flexural testing was conducted on Lloyd's instruments LRX and Izod impact test was conducted on Ceast Instruments with notched samples. Transmission electron microscopy (TEM) is used to get a direct evidence of the structure and spatial dispersion of clay layers. TEM images were observed with JEOL (JEM1200EX) instrument. Sample for TEM was prepared using a temperature controlled Leica Ultra cut UCT microtome machine. Extruded pellets were placed in an arm, which is attached to a motor controlled hand wheel. As the arm moves vertically pass the diamond knife, the sample is cut into required thickness. Entire operation carried out at 60 °C. The cut sections are directly transferred to copper grid with the help of sucrose solution, which subsequently dried before being transferred to TEM instrument. The ultra thin sections of thickness 70-100 nm were then used to ascertain the dispersion of clay layers in the polymer matrix.

4.3. Results and Discussion

4.3.1. FTIR and PXRD of Cloisite 20 A and DODA 90

FT-IR spectra of cloisite 20 A and DODA 90 are shown in Figure 4.1. Peaks at 3620 and 3698 cm^{-1} are due to -OH band stretch for Al-OH, Mg-OH and Si-OH. The shoulders and broadness of the -OH bands are mainly due to contributions of several structural -OH groups occurring in MMT. The overlaid absorption peaks in the region of 1640 cm^{-1} in the FT-IR spectrum is attributed to -OH bending mode of water (adsorbed water). IR peaks at 915, 875 and 836 cm^{-1} are attributed to AlAlOH, AlFeOH and AlMgOH bending vibration respectively. Peaks at 2940 and 2850 cm^{-1} for organoclays, are ascribed to the asymmetric and symmetric vibration of methylene groups $(CH_2)_n$ of the aliphatic carbon chain. In addition, there is also HCH stretching vibration band at 1465 cm^{-1} in the IR spectrum of

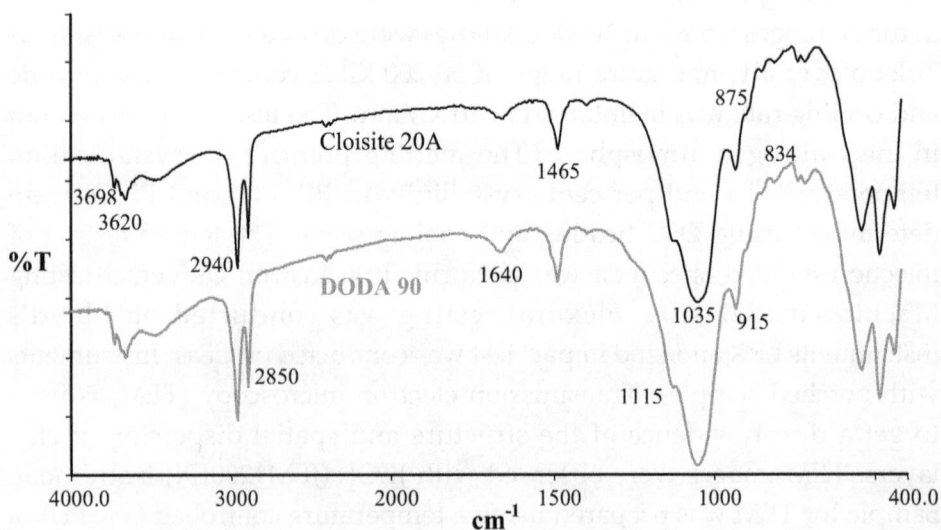

Figure 4.1. FT-IR spectra of Cloisite 20 A and DODA 90.

organoclays. FT-IR studies clearly indicate the formation of organic–inorganic hybrids.

The PXRD of pattern of DODA 90 and Cloisite 20A is shown in Figure 4.2. The peak around 2.7° and 3.8° is corresponds to [001] plane. The basal spacing, d_{001} is 3.3 and 2.4 nm for DODA 90 and Cloisite 20A, respectively. The lower basal spacing of Cloisite 20A reveals that the organic modifier (DMDAC) used in the Cloisite 20A has shorter alkyl chain compared to the organic modifier used for DODA 90. The intensity of the peak for DODA 90 is also lower than Cloisite 20A, demonstrates the high crystalline character of the MMT used for Cloisite 20A. The change in crystallinity arises mainly due to origin of MMT. The MMT used for Cloisite 20A is originated from Wyoming, USA while MMT used for DODA 90 is from Rajasthan, India.

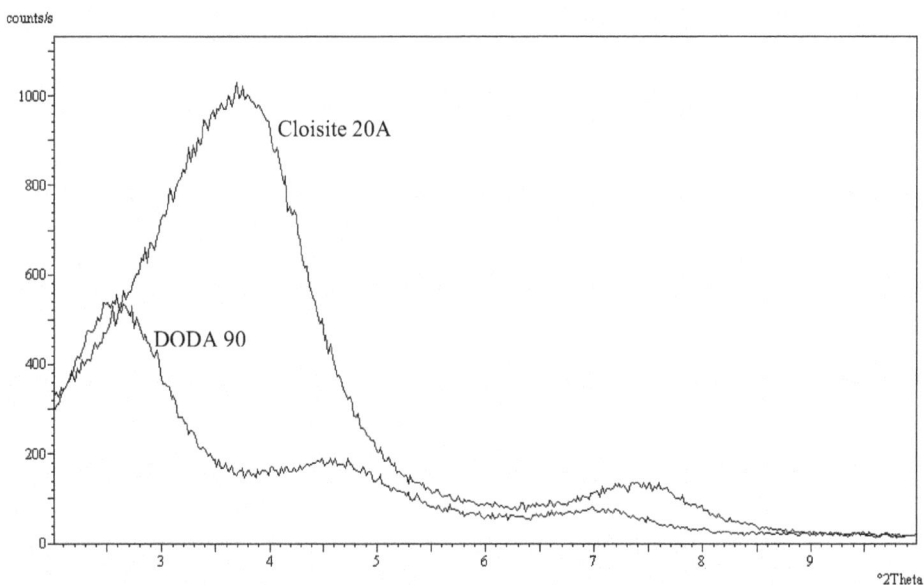

Figure 4.2. PXRD patter of Cloisite 20A and DODA 90.

4.3.2. Particle Size Distribution and Thermal Stability of Cloisite 20 A and DODA 90

The particle size of the nanoclays is an important parameter to form PNCs because with finer particles of nanoclays requires lower time for compounding and ease in the processing of PNCs. However, the average particle size of Cloisite 20A and DODA is 8 and 9 μm, respectively; the particle size distribution of DODA 90 is broader than Cloisite 20A. Though the size of the both nanoclays are in the unit of microns, the nanoclay term for these microns particles are given because of its single micron particle contains thousands of nano-platelets and which are easily expanded in the organic matrix. The narrow particle size distribution resulted into almost identical size of the filler which can result better mechanical properties than fillers with broader particle size distribution. It is clear from the Figure 4.3 that the Cloisite 20A has narrow particle size distribution while DODA 90 has slightly broader particle size distribution.

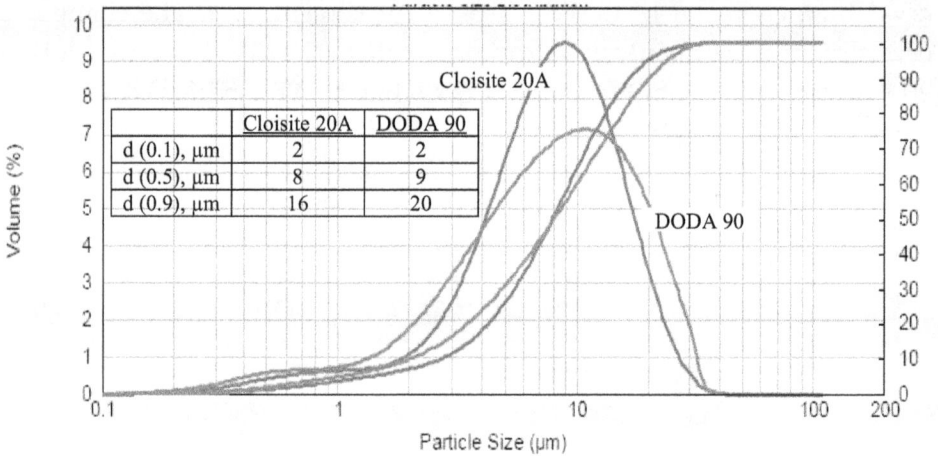

	Cloisite 20A	DODA 90
d (0.1), µm	2	2
d (0.5), µm	8	9
d (0.9), µm	16	20

Figure 4.3. Particle size distribution of Cloisite 20A and DODA 90.

As the melt compounding of PP and nanoclays is the economically viable method, it is necessary for nanoclay to withstand high processing temperature. In this study we have compounded PP with nanoclay at 190-200 °C, therefore, it is prime requirement to study whether these nanoclays are stable up to that temperature or not. Thermogravimetric analysis of nanoclays is shown in Figure 4.4. The Cloisite 20A and DODA 90 is started to degrade at about 190 °C and 210 °C temperature, respectively. The higher thermal stability of DODA 90 over Cloisite 20A is due to higher alkyl chain length in organic modifier used for DODA 90. From this study, we can say that the both nanoclays can withstand PNCs processing temperature.

4.3.3. PP/nanoclay nanocomposites (PNCs)

The WAXD patterns were used to determine increase in the basal spacing [001] of the nanoclays thereby confirming the intercalation of the

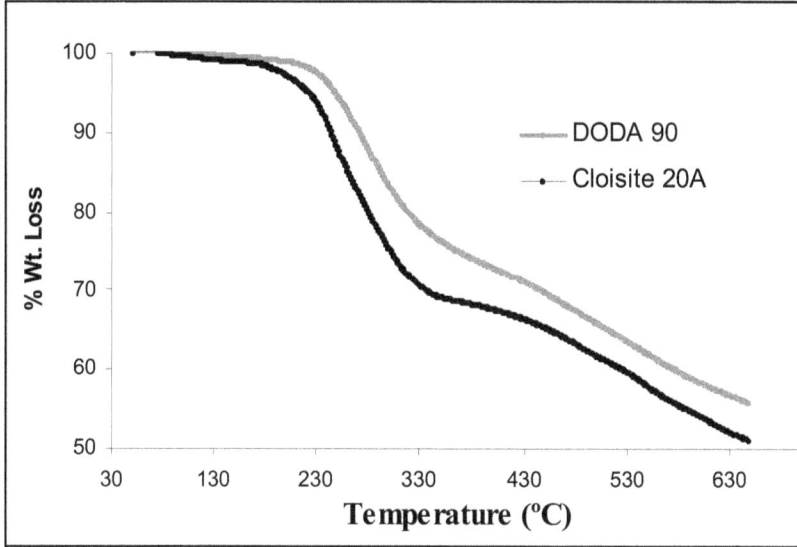

Figure 4.4. Thermogravimetric analysis of Cloisite 20A and DODA 90.

PP in the nanoclay layers. The results are presented in Figure 4.5. The change in the basal spacing of Cloisite 20A and DODA 90 after compounding with PP and MA-g-PP is 0.19 nm and 0.17 nm, respectively. The change in the basal spacing clearly indicates the intercalation of PP and MA-g-PP into nanoclays. The XRD peaks shifted to lower angles

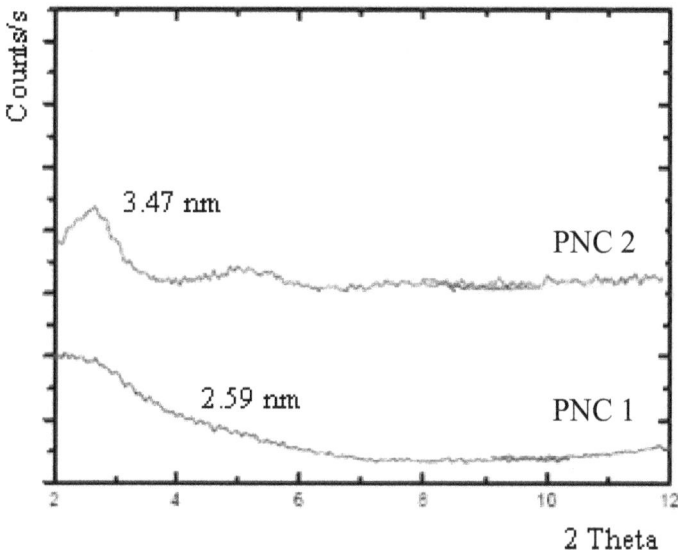

Figure 4.5. Comparison of basal spacing of nanoclays after compounding.

suggested that both intercalated and partly exfoliated nanocomposites were formed. The interlayer expansion depends mainly on the compatibility between the polymer and the organic intercalant or clay attribute or both and the chemical interaction between the two phases. Nevertheless, the intensity of the XRD peak does decrease with the reduction of intercalant coverage.

Reduction of the X-ray peak intensity can be caused by different factors, but the two more important ones in this case should be either the reduction of the intercalated nanoclays aggregates due to exfoliation or the compaction of the nanoclays to form large aggregates. To verify the cause of the peak intensity reduction, TEM observations were conducted.

The TEM images in Figure 4.6 reveal the structures for PNC 1 and PNC 2. The dark and bright regions correspond to the nanoclays and PP matrix, respectively. The images clearly show the existence of nanoclay clusters in PNC 2, indicating a poor clay dispersion and disordered structure. Poor dispersion was also seen for PNC 1 but lower than PNC 2. However, in contrast with PNC 1, these clusters possess a well aligned structure. These reconfirm the XRD results for the poor nanoclay intercalation and dispersion. No sign of partial exfoliation can be observed, and so the reduction in the peak intensity of the PNCs is more likely due to agglomeration.

Table 4.2. Thermal properties of PP, PPB and PNCs.

Samples	ΔH_f Corrected (cal/g)	Per cent Crystallinity	T_m (ºC)	Crystallization Temp. T_c (ºC)
PP	13.9	27.9	162.8	112.0
PPB	15.9	32.0	162.1	114.3
PNC 1	17.1	34.3	163.3	116.5
PNC 2	15.7	31.6	163.0	113.3

DSC measurements of PP, PPB, PNC 1 and PNC 2 were carried out to determine the effect of intercalant type and intercalant coverage on the crystallization behavior. The melting and crystallization parameters determined from heating and cooling scans are presented in Table 4.2. PP is a semi-crystalline polymer containing both amorphous phase and crystalline phases simultaneously. Crystalline domain is the ordered

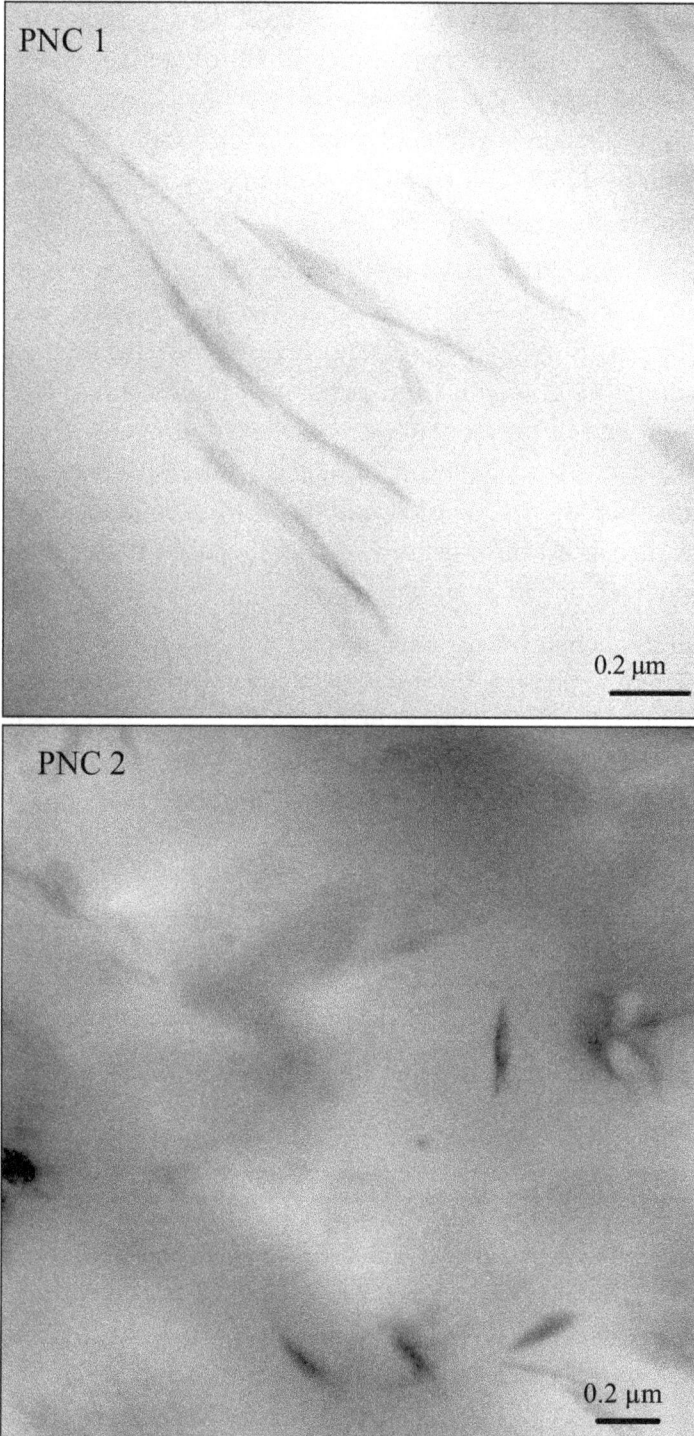

Figure 4.6. TEM images of PNC 1 and PNC 2.

structure developed by certain factor. Some times presence of dispersed layered nanoclays changes crystallinity in PP by acting as a nucleating agent. The highest crystallinity is observed for PNC 1 while PPB and PNC 2 have almost similar crystallinity. Similarly, the crystallization temperature is observed to be 116.5 °C for PNC 1, while other samples has T_c within the temperature range of 112-114.2 °C.

The addition of nanoclays in PP is accelerating the crystallization process, but not noticeable increase in the crystallinity is observed. Probably, the partial exfoliation of nanoclay increases the nucleation effect and accelerates the crystallization process, while on the other hand, in PNCs, the confined PP segment in the nanoclay interlayer will be restricted, resulting in a decrease in the number of crystalline PP chains. In addition, the absorption of the PP or compatibilizer molecules on the nanoclay surface may also affect the crystallization behavior of PNCs. Nevertheless, this issue still remains to be understood.

The static mechanical properties for PP, PPB and PNCs are listed in Table 4.3. There is increase in the tensile strength by 18 and 20 per cent, tensile modulus 41 and 39 per cent for PNC 1 and PNC 2, respectively with respect to PP. The flexural modulus for PNC 1 and PNC 2 is also increases by 23 and 22 per cent by incorporation of 5 per cent nanoclay in PP along with 5 per cent MA-g-PP.

Table 4.3. Mechanical properties of PP, PPB and PCNs.

Samples	Tensile Strength (MPa)	Tensile Modulus (MPa)	Flexural Strength (MPa)	Flexural Modulus (MPa)	Izod Impact Strength (J/m)
PP	21.6	1110	30.2	910	86
PPB	25.2	1291	33.6	990	81
PNC 1	25.5	1570	33.9	1120	57
PNC 2	25.9	1541	36.0	1117	59

Increase in tensile and flexural modulus was consistently observed on repeated testing. The increase of modulus is attributable to the reinforcement effect. In general, for inorganic particle-reinforced polymer, the particle–matrix interaction is an important factor in determining the ultimate mechanical properties of composites because a weak interface would lower the material integrity and reduce the yield strength. Yield strength of nanoclay-reinforced PP was higher than neat PP and PPB, which is indicative of significant interaction between nanoclay particles and the PP matrix. The impact strength of PPB and PNCs is observed to decrease with addition of nanoclays and polybond 3200 in the PP matrix. This suggests that reinforcement of PP with nanoclays along with polybond 3200 negatively influence the impact strength. The impact strength can be retained in spite of increase in modulus due to reinforcement of PP with nanoclay by using elastomers toughened PP rather than neat PP.

4.4. Nanoclays for Paints

In the past, paints, lacquers and varnishes have contained about 80 per cent solvent. The thickening effect in such paints, lacquers and varnishes is achieved mostly by solvent evaporation. There is a trend in the industry in which manufacturers of such systems move from high solvent systems to higher solids systems to comply with stricter environmental limits on volatile organic emissions. Since there is less solvent in such systems, there is a need to modify the rheological properties of the particular system by use of a thickener which will impart sag resistance and shear thinning behavior without reducing the clarity and gloss of the coating [35-39].

Organoclay is formed when MMT is made to react with different types of quaternary ammonium organic compounds. The type of quaternary ammonium salts used for the organoclay are determine the compatibility of the resulting organoclay in different solvents and resin systems, where slight differences in the polarity play an important role. Due to organophilic nature of organoclays, they are not swell in water as the MMT. Organoclay can be dispersed in organic solvents and cause the formation of a gel structure. The dispersion process is determined by the effect of the solvent on the organic chains on the quaternary compound and with the mechanical energy given by shearing the product during the dispersion process. The thixotropic behavior of organoclays is used widely in almost all of the solvent based coatings. Settling, sagging and leveling of solvent based paints are controlled by the appropriate addition of small amount of organoclays. Each formulation containing binders, solvents, extenders and pigments could be influenced differently by the organoclay addition, so that the proper grade, dosage and way of incorporation must initially be determined.

In this part of the chapter, we have studied the effect of organoclay addition in different solvents on stability of the gel volume with respect to time. The objective behind this work is to study the applicability of organoclays which are prepared from Indian bentonite. The study emphasizes on dispersion of organoclays in solvents with different polarity.

4.4.1. Materials and Methods

The organoclays used for this study are OC 8 [CH$_3$(CH$_2$)$_{15}$(CH$_3$)$_3$ N – MMT], OC 3 [(HT)$_2$(CH$_3$)$_2$ N – MMT] and OC 7 [C$_6$H$_5$CH$_2$(CH$_2$)$_{17}$(CH$_3$)$_2$ N – MMT]. The synthesis and characterization of these three organoclays are given in chapter 3. The solvents used are toluene, carbon tetrachloride, chloroform, pyridine, benzene, tetrahydrofuran, ethanol, acetone and diethyl ether purchased from s.d. fine chem., India.

For measurement of gel volume, organoclay added into 100 mL solvents in a cylinder. The dispersion is then ultrasonicated for 10 min. and noted the results as cm^3 after selected time period.

4.5. Results and Discussion

The solvent solubility parameters of different solvents are shown in Table 4.4. With Hansen's solubility parameters [40-42], $\delta_o^2 = \delta_d^2 + \delta_p^2 + \delta_h^2$, the correlation between the degree of exfoliation of organoclays and the solvent in which the clay platelets are dispersed can be analyzed.

Table 4.4. Solvent solubility parameters of different solvents[a].

Solvent	δ_o	δ_d	δ_p	δ_h	H-bonding Group
Pyridine	10.61	9.25	4.3	2.9	strong
Benzene	9.15	8.95	0.5	1.0	weak
Toluene	8.91	8.82	0.7	1.0	weak
Carbon tetrachloride	8.65	8.65	0	0	weak
Chloroform	9.21	8.65	1.5	2.8	weak
Tetrahydrofuran	9.52	8.22	2.8	3.9	moderate
Ethanol	12.92	7.73	4.3	9.5	strong
Acetone	9.77	7.58	5.1	3.4	moderate
Diethyl ether	7.62	7.05	1.4	2.5	moderate
Water	23.5	6.0	15.3	16.7	strong

[a]Hansen's solubility parameters, $\delta_o^2 = \delta_d^2 + \delta_p^2 + \delta_h^2$, where δ_o is total solubility parameter, δ_d is component due to dispersion forces, δ_p is component due to polar forces and δ_h is component due to H-bonding. All the solvent solubility parameters have units of (cal/cm^3)$^{1/2}$.

It has been found that the dispersion force of the solvent, reflected by δ_d, is the principal factor determining whether the clay platelets remain suspended in the solvent while the polar (δ_p) and hydrogen-bonding (δ_h) forces affect primarily the tactoids formation of the suspended platelets. The organoclays studied are precipitated in solvents with molecules with moderately strong hydrogen-bonding groups as shown in Table 4.5. The gel volumes are measured by dispersing 2 g of organoclays in 100 mL solvent. Simultaneously, the dispersions were ultrasonicated for 10 min and gel volume was measure after 24 h.

Table 4.5. Gel volume of organoclays (OC 3, OC 7 and OC 8) in different solvents.

Solvent	Gel Volume (cm³) after 24 h		
	OC 8	OC 3	OC 7
Pyridine	10	14	32
Benzene	18	24	34
Toluene	20	32	20
Carbon tetrachloride	36	100	30
Chloroform	90	96	100
Tetrahydrofuran	10	12	100
Ethanol	10	12	12
Acetone	8	14	8
Diethylether	4	8	14
Methanol	10	16	6

The precipitation effect is correlated with decrease in the gel volume. OC 7 is completely exfoliated in chloroform and tetrahydrouran. OC 3 is completely exfoliated in carbon tetrachloride while partially exfoliated in chloroform. OC 8 is partially exfoliated in chloroform and moderately in carbon tetrachloride. The stability of gel in these solvents also suggests that these organoclays can be useful for the paint formulations. To study the effect of concentration of organoclay in solvent and time period on gel volume we have used toluene as solvent for further study.

The effect of organoclay concentration in toluene on the gel volume is shown in Figure 4.7. As the concentration of organoclays increases the gel volume increases linearly due to partition phenomenon of solvent with organic modifier situated at the surface of MMT. The highest gel volume

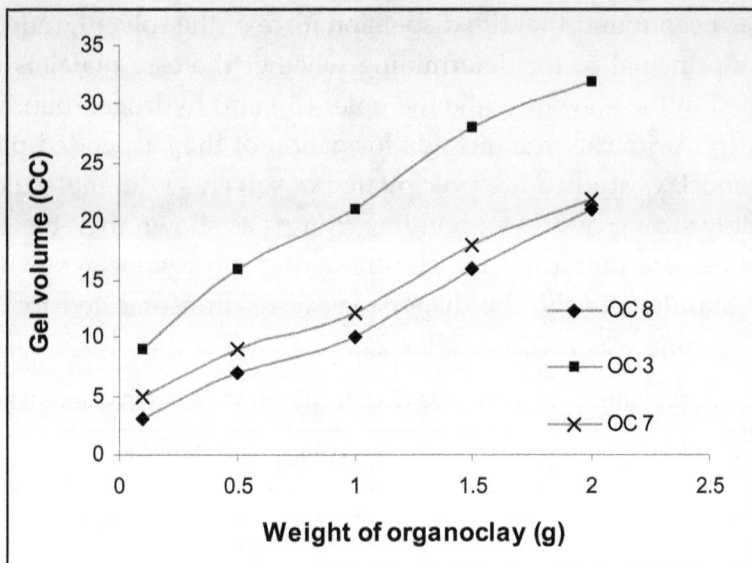

Figure 4.7. Effect of concentration of organoclays in toluene on gel volume (toluene: 100 mL; ultrasonication: 10 min; time: 24 h).

of 32 cm^3 is observed for 2 g of OC 3 in 100 mL of toluene. The gel volume for OC 7 and OC 8 is 21 cm^3. It is clear from the value of gel volume that the OC 3 is partially exfoliated and OC 7 and OC 8 are precipitated.

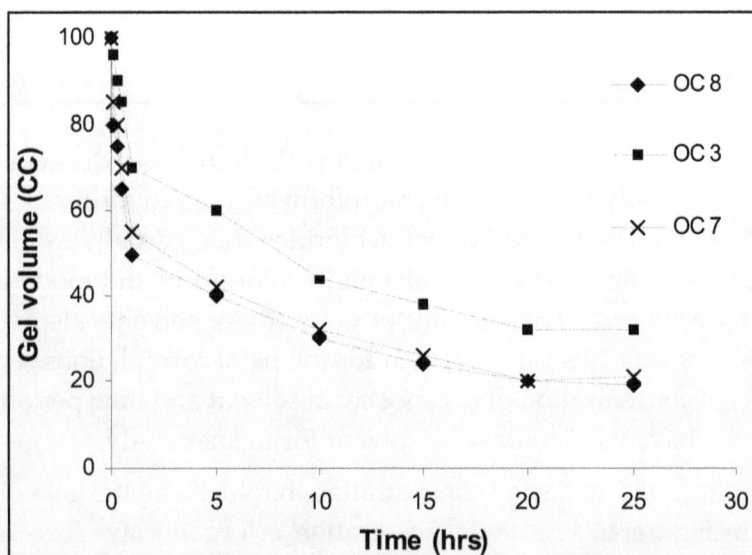

Figure 4.8. Effect of time on stability of gel volume (toluene: 100 mL; organoclays: 2 g; ultrasonication: 10 min; time: 24 h).

The stability of gels is an important parameter for application of these gels in paints and resins. As shown in Figure 4.8, the gel volume is decreases with time and also decrease in the gel volume is faster within 5 h. After 20 h, gel attained stability. The higher gel volume of OC 3 is attributed to organic modifier which contained two long alkyl chains. Organic modifier used for OC 7 and OC 8 have single long alkyl chain therefore the organophilicity of OC 3 is higher as compared to OC 7 and OC 8 which results into higher gel volume. However, it should be noted that organoclays will result different property in application such as paint because paint formulation required fillers and resins in addition to organoclays.

References

1. Okada A. and Usuki A., *Mater. Sci. Engg. C*, 3, 109, 1995.

2. Alexandre M. and Dubois P., *Mater. Sci. Engg.*, 28, 1, 2000.

3. Fischer H., *Mater. Sci. Engg. C*, 23, 763, 2003.

4. Ray S. S. and Okamoto M., *Prog. Polym. Sci.*, 28, 1539, 2003.

5. Ray S. S. and Bousmina M., *Prog. Mater. Sci.*, 50, 962, 2005.

6. Okamoto M., *Int. Polym. Process. XXI*, 5, 487, 2006.

7. Zhang S. and Horrocks R., *Prog. Polym. Sci.*, 28, 1517, 2003.

8. Gao F., *Mater. today*, 50, November 2004.

9. Tjong S. C., Mater. Sci. Engg. R, 41, 1, 2003.

10. Carrado K. A., *Appl. Clay Sci.*, 17, 1, 2000.

11. Kojima Y., Usuki A., Kawasumi M., Okada A., Fukushima Y., Kurauchi T. T. and Kamigaito O., *J. Mater. Res.*, 8, 1179, 1993.

12. Kojima Y., Usuki A., Kawasumi M., Okada A., Kurauchi T. T., Kamigaito O., *J. Polym. Sci. Part A: Polym. Chem.*, 31, 983, 1993.

13. Giannelis E. P., *Adv. Muter.*, 8(1), 29, 1996.

14. Bergman J. S., Chen H., Giannelis E. P., Thomasc M. G. and Coates G. W., *Chem. Commun.*, 2179, 1999.

15. Garces J. M., Moll D. J., Bicerano J., Fibiger R. and McLeod D. G., *Adv. Mater.*, 12(23), 1835, 2000.

16. Morgan A. B., *Polym. Adv. Technol.*, 17, 206, 2006.

17. Wang J., Severtson S. J. and Stein A., *Adv. Mater.*, 18, 1585, 2006.

18. James Lee L., Zeng C., Cao X., Han X., Shen J. and Xu G., *Compos. Sci. Techn.*, 65, 2344, 2005.

19. Gusev A. A. and Lusti H. R., *Adv. Mater.*, 13 (21), 1641, 2001.

20. Zeng Q. H., Yu A. B. (Max) Lu G. Q. and Paul D. R., *J. Nanosci. Nanotech.*, 5 (10), 1574, 2005.

21. Bartholmai M. and Schartel B., *Polym. Adv. Technol.*, 15, 355, 2004.

22. Thostenson E. T., Li C. and Chou T.-W., *Compos. Sci. Techn.*, 65, 491, 2005.

23. Reichert P., Nitz H., Klinke S., Brandsch R., Thomann R. and Mulhaupt R., *Macromol. Mater. Eng.*, 275, 8, 2000.

24. Arroyo M., Suarez R. V., Herrero B. and Lopez-Manchado M. A., *J. Mater. Chem.*, 13, 2915, 2003.

25. Patel H. A., Somani R. S., Bajaj H. C. and Jasra R.V., *Bull. Mater. Sci.*, 29(2), 133, 2006.

26. Jimenez G., Ogata N., Kawai H. and Ogihara T., *J. Appl. Polym. Sci.*, 64, 2211, 1997.

27. Messersmith P. and Giannelis E., J. *Polym. Sci. Part A: Polym. Chem.*, 33, 1047, 1995.

28. Reichert P., Hoffmann B., Bock T., Thomann R. and Mulhaupt R., *Macromol. Rapid Commun.*, 22, 519, 2001.

29. Liu X. and Wu Q., *Polymer*, 42, 1001, 2001.

30. Ton-That M.-T., Perrin-Sarazin F., Cole K. C., Bureau M. and Denault J., *Polym. Eng. Sci.*, 44, 1212, 2004.

31. Wang Y., Chen F., Li Y. and Wu K., *Compos. B*, 35, 111, 2004.

32. Manias E., Touny A., Wu L., Strawhecker K., Lu B. and Chung T. C., *Chem. Mater.*, 13, 3516, 2001.

33. Utracki L. A., Sepehr M. and Li J., *Int. Polym. Process.*, 1, 3, 2006.

34. Okada A., Usuki A., *Macromol. Mater. Eng.*, 291, 1449 (2006).

35. Edwin S., *US Patent 509859*, 1990.

36. Gadberry J. F, Hoey M. and Powell C. F., *US Patent 5663111*, 1997.

37. Somani R. S, Shukla D. B, Bhalala B. J, Mehta A. S and Jasra R. V, *Technical Report*, Indian Oil Corporation, R&D Centre, Faridabad, 1998.

38. Somani R. S, Shukla D. B and Bhalala B. J., *Indian Patent*, NF No. 572/DEL/2000, 2000.

39. Tatum J. P. and Wright R. C., *US Patent 4752342*, 1988.

40. Hanley H. J. M., Muzny C. D., Ho D. L., Glinka C. J. and Manias E., *Inter. J. Thermophys.*, 22 (5), 1435, 2001.

41. Ho D. L., Briber R. M., and Glinka C. J., *Chem. Mater.*, 13, 1923, 2001.

42. Ho D. L. and Glinka C. J., *Chem. Mater.*, 15, 1309, 2003.

Chapter 5

Synthesis of Metal Nanoparticles (Pd, Rh, Au and Ag) Anchored on Nanoclays

5.1. Introduction

The physical properties of nanoscale particles are significantly different from those of microscopic or readily crystallizing materials of identical chemical composition. The interest in the synthesis of metal nanoparticles has been growing because of their unique electronic, optical, thermal, and catalytic properties and promising applications in interdisciplinary fields [1]. Palladium, rhodium, gold and silver metal nanoparticles based catalysts are employed in variety of catalytic reactions, as the catalytic activity and selectivity is usually influenced by the particle size of the metals. Since nanoparticles tend to be fairly unstable in solution, common methods for stabilizing and controlling their size employ the use of capping agents such as surfactants, ligands, polymers or dendrimers [2-3].

Montmorillonite (MMT) and organically modified MMT have been extensively used as catalyst supports in wide range of heterogeneous catalysis system [4-6]. Palladium nanoparticles have been synthesized by preparing Pd hydrosols in alkyl ammonium surfactants solution, which is then added to MMT [8-15]. Kaolinite [16], Activated carbon [17], carbon nanotubes [18], SiO_2 [19], Al_2O_3 [20] and many other solids are also reported as supporting materials for growing palladium and rhodium metal nanoparticles and these are widely used as heterogeneous catalysts in industries. Kiraly *et al.*, have reported in situ generation of Pd metal nanoparticles in smectite clay by preparation of Pd hydrosol prior to intercalation in MMT and using binary liquid mixture [1-2]. MMT is hydrophilic in nature with a high cation exchange capacity, which made MMT a very useful material in various applications. As such Pd^{2+} and Rh^{3+} ions are very difficult to exchange completely with interlayer cations (Na^+, Ca^{++} or K^+) present in MMT. The complete exchange has been reported to be achieved by ion exchanging reaction for several days under condensation. To overcome this problem, the metal halide salts are converted in to water soluble metal complex to facilitate faster ion exchange.

Gold nanoparticles have attracted much attention due to their applicability as oxidative catalyst at reasonably low temperature [21-24]. Different wet chemical methods have been used for the synthesis of metallic nanoparticles, the most common involving the reduction of metal salts in surfactant solutions using a reducing agent such as sodium citrate or sodium borohydride. The citrate method results into relatively large metallic particles due to weak reducing efficiency in comparison to sodium borohydride, known for fast nucleation and surfactants drastically inhibits growth [25]. Varied shapes and sizes by seeding growth of gold nanoparticles in quaternary ammonium surfactants using different reducing agents have been reported in the literature [26-28]. To support gold and silver nanoparticles on a stable inorganic or organic matrix is a prime requirement in applications such as catalysis. Varieties of supports such as SiO_2, TiO_2, Al_2O_3, Fe_2O_3, carbon, clay and polymer for stabilizing gold nanoparticles have been reported [29-31]. There are fewer references available that demonstrate gold nanoparticles supported on MMT. Paek *et al.*, [32] have synthesized gold pillared alumino silicates by capping the charged gold nanoparticles using N,N,N-Trimethyl (11-mercaptoundecyl) ammonium ion as protecting ligands and studied the effect of calcination on the size of gold nanoparticles. In other report, Chen *et al.*, [33] have adsorbed polyethyleneimine on MMT, subsequently added gold salt which were reduced by polyethyleneimine itself. They have also illustrated the effect of pH on the particle size of generated gold nanoparticles. Aihara *et al.*, [34] have described the synthesis of gold and silver nanoparticles in Laponite using gold-amine-nitrate complex and silver nitrate as gold and silver precursor respectively.

The present chapter discusses a promising approach for the controlled synthesis of Pd and Rh metal nanoparticles supported on MMT and partially organically modified MMT (POMM) using [Pd (NH$_3$)$_4$] Cl$_2$ and [Rh (NH$_3$)$_6$] Cl$_3$ - complex by eliminating the preparation of Pd and Rh hydrosol in surfactants prior to intercalation in MMT. The studies also show the effect of organic modification of MMT on particle size of Pd and Rh metals. There have not been any report demonstrating single pot synthesis of gold and silver nanoparticles anchored on organoclay. The objective behind this study was to synthesize gold and silver nanoparticles supported organoclays. The effect of reduction path, concentration and type of surfactants on the particle size of gold and silver nanoparticles anchored organoclay is also studied.

5.2. Experimental Section

5.2.1. Materials

Bentonite was collected from Barmer district of Rajasthan (India). Palladium chloride (PdCl$_2$) and rhodium chloride, hydrated (RhCl$_3$—XH$_2$O), hydrogentetrachloroaurate trihydrate (HAuCl$_4$·3H$_2$O), silver nitrate (AgNO$_3$), hexadecyltrimethylammonium bromide [CH$_3$(CH$_2$)$_{15}$ N(Br)(CH$_3$)$_3$], dioctadecyldimethylammonium chloride [(CH$_3$(CH$_2$)$_{17}$)$_2$ N(Cl)(CH$_3$)$_2$] and sodium borohydride (NaBH$_4$) were procured from Sigma-Aldrich (USA) and used as received. Liquor ammonia (25 per cent NH$_3$) was from s. d. fine chemical, India and dimethyldi-hydrogenatedt allow ammonium chloride from Cutch oil, India and was used as received. The [Pd(NH$_3$)$_4$]Cl$_2$ and [Rh(NH$_3$)$_6$]Cl$_3$ solutions were prepared by treating a solution containing equal amount of water and liquor ammonia with PdCl$_2$ and RhCl$_3$—X H$_2$O. The both the solutions were evaporated on a steam bath until only a faint odor of ammonia is noticeable. The resulted light yellow solutions were filtered and cooled in an ice bath to 10 – 15 C [35].

Bentonite was purified by sedimentation technique discussed in earlier [36]. 1.5 per cent w/v clay slurry made in deionized water and supernant of less then 2 µm fractions was collected after pre-calculated time, height at room temperature (30C). The clay slurry was dried and ground into fine powder. The chemical composition of the purified MMT was: 55.9 per cent SiO_2, 20.9 per cent Al_2O_3, 9.15 per cent Fe_2O_3, 2.1 per cent MgO, 2.8 per cent CaO, 0.71 per cent K_2O and 0.73 per cent Na_2O with loss on ignition of 7.7 per cent. The cation exchange capacity was measured by standard ammonium acetate method at pH 7 and was found to be 0.90 meq/g of MMT.

5.2.2. Synthesis of Pd and Rh Nanoparticles in MMT and POMM

The POMM samples were typically synthesized by dispersing 20 g of MMT in 2 L distilled water and exchanging 25, 50 and 75 per cent of exchangeable cations with dimethyldihydrogenatedtallowammonium cation under vigorous stirring at 80 C temperature for 1 h. The resulting partially organically modified MMT was filtered, washed until free from halide ion (tested with 0.01M $AgNO_3$ solution) and dried, yielded off white powder and were designated as HT 25, HT 50 and HT 75 respectively.

To 5 g each of purified montmorillonite (MMT) dispersed in 200 mL distilled water (2.5 per cent w/v) and stirred to facilitate complete dispersion for 1 h, were added 40 mL (0.9 meq Pd or Rh/g of MMT) tetraammine palladium (II) and hexaammine rhodium (III) solution portion wise with continuous stirring for another 1 h at room temperature (30 C), to obtain $[Pd(NH_3)_4]$ – MMT and $[Rh(NH_3)_6]$ – MMT respectively. The Pd and Rh metal complex supported MMT were subsequently reduced using sodium borohydride at room temperature, which results a grayish-black dispersion. The Pd and Rh-MMT were filtered, washed, dried at 60 C for 5 hrs in vacuum oven and ground into fine powder. The Pd and Rh metal nanoparticles supported HT 25, HT 50 and HT 75 were synthesized by using 5 g of each POMM (HT 25, HT 50 and HT 75) as supporting materials and exchanged with metal cations (75, 50 and 25 per cent Pd and Rh respectively) in iso-butyl alcohol. As POMM is both hydrophilic and hydrophobic in nature and resulted into poor dispersion in distilled water, iso-butyl alcohol was used to facilitate dispersion. The iso-butyl alcohol also acts as a reducing agent and can facilitate reduction of Pd^{+2} and Rh^{+3} ions to zero valent metals during the reduction of metal ions with sodium borohydride. The schematic representation of formation of Pd and Rh metal nanoparticles in MMT and partially organically modified MMT (POMM) are illustrated in Figure 5.1.

5.2.3. Synthesis of Gold and Silver Nanoparticles Anchored Organoclays

Gold and silver nanoparticles supported on organoclay were synthesized following different reduction paths as shown in Figure 5.2. In Path 1, 25 mg of $HAuCl_4$ were added in 0.39 g of hexadecyltrimethylammonium bromide (HDTA) dissolved in 500 mL deionized water at 80 °C. The gold salt in HDTA solution was then reduced by addition of freshly prepared $NaBH_4$ solution (50 mg in 10 mL deionized water). This resulted into wine red solution. 125 mL MMT slurry (1 per cent w/v) was added to the solution at rate of 2.8 mL/min with vigorous stirring at 353 K for 45 min. The resultant gold-organoclay hybrid was filtered, washed with deionized water and dried at 333 K and was designated as M3HDTG. A 5 per cent w/w (130 mg $HAuCl_4$) gold nanoparticles supported organoclay was synthesized by similar procedure and denoted as M5HDTG.

In path 2, the reduction was performed after the intercalation of HDTA containing $HAuCl_4$. 25 mg of $HAuCl_4$ was added in 500 mL HDTA solution. 125 mL MMT slurry (1 per cent w/v) was added to the solution at rate of 2.8 mL/min with vigorous stirring at 353 K for 45 min. The resultant gold salt-organoclay hybrid reduced by addition of freshly prepared $NaBH_4$ solution, formed gold-organoclay hybrid which was subsequently filtered, washed with deionized water and dried at 60 °C and denoted as M4HDTG (1 per cent Au). We have also used dioctadecyldimethylammonium chloride (DODA), which contains two long alkyl chains to study the effect of surfactant used in organoclay on size and shape of nanoparticles. The organoclay samples with 1 per cent loading of gold were synthesized by both paths as described above; 0.62 g DODA dissolved in 500 mL deionized water and 25 mg $HAuCl_4$ were used, designated as M1DODG (Path 1) and M2DODG (Path 2). The silver nanoparticles loaded organoclays were synthesized using procedure similar to that used for gold nanoparticles as discussed above. $AgNO_3$ was used as a precursor for silver nanoparticles. The samples obtained for silver nanoparticles anchored organoclays are designated as M1DODS (1

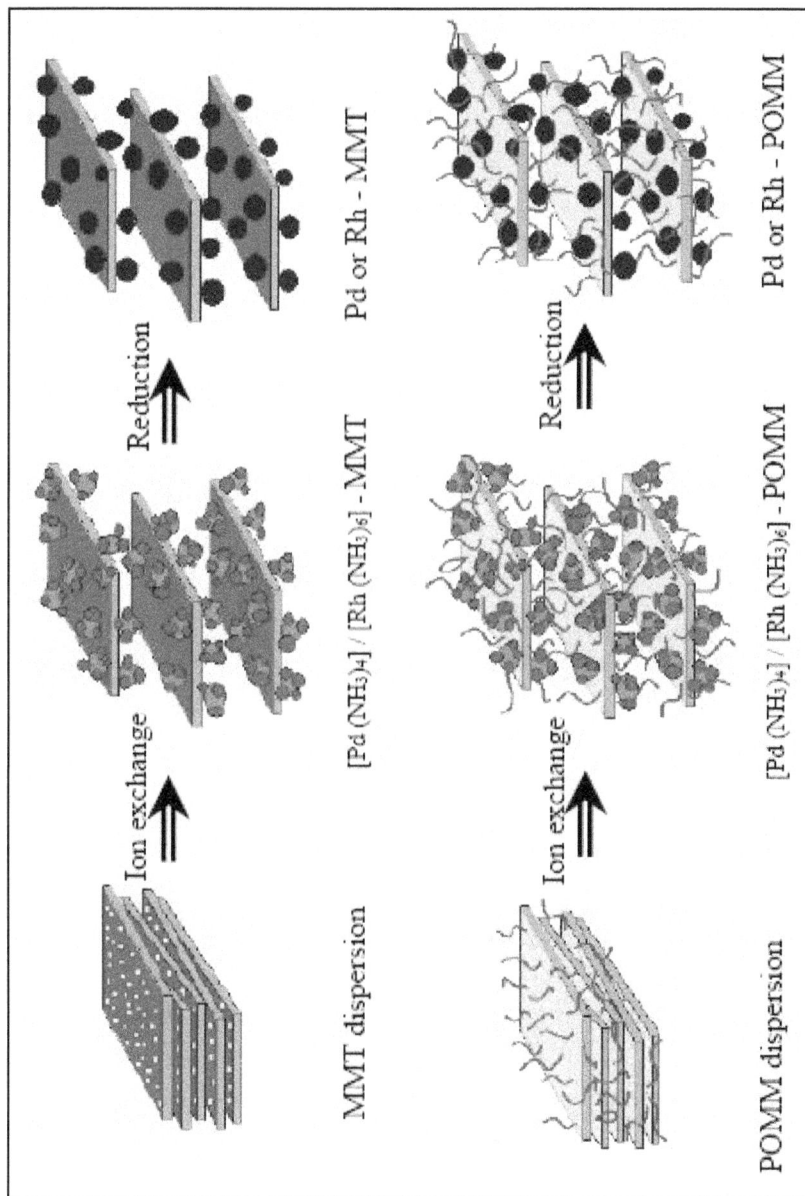

Figure 5.1. Schematic representation of formation of Pd and Rh nanoparticles supported MMT and partially organically modified MMT (POMM).

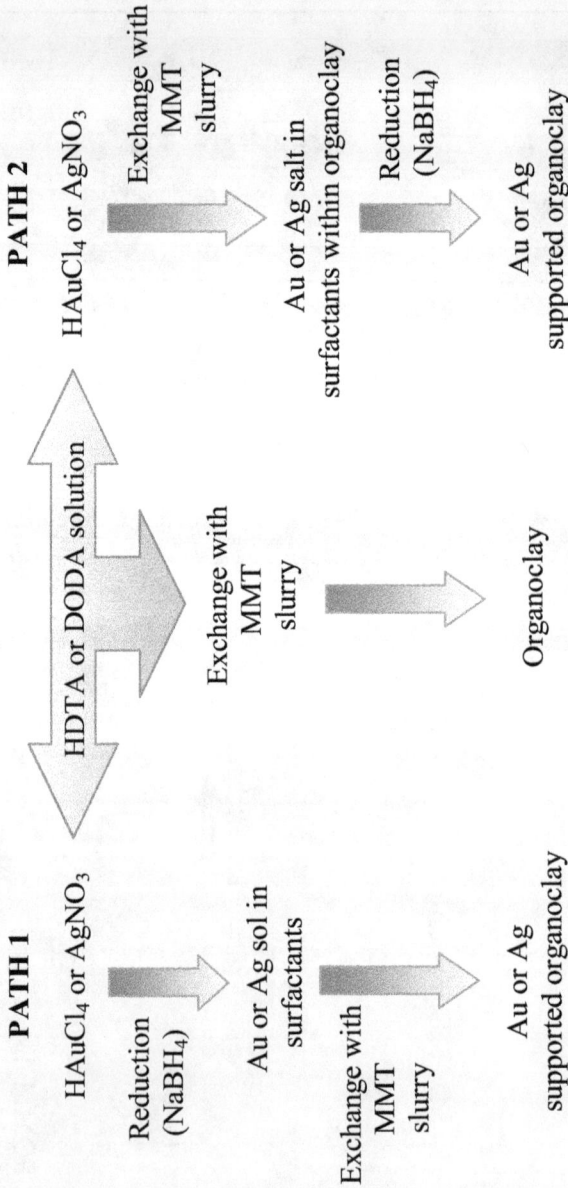

Figure 5.2. Schematic representation of synthetic route for Au and Ag nanoparticles anchored organoclay.

per cent w/w; Path 1; DODA), M2DODS (1 per cent w/w; Path 2; DODA), M3HDTS (1 per cent w/w; Path 1; HDTA), M4HDTS (1 per cent w/w; Path 2; HDTA), and M5HTDS (5 per cent w/w; Path 1; HDTA). The organoclays without gold and silver loading (denoted as MHDT and MDOD) were also synthesized using same amount of HDTA and DODA under identical reaction conditions for comparison with gold and silver-organoclay hybrids.

5.2.4. Characterizations

Palladium, rhodium, gold and silver content were estimated using Perkin-Elmer *Optima 2000 DV* ICP-AES. Powder X-ray diffraction (PXRD) analysis was carried out with a Phillips powder diffractometer *X' Pert MPD* using PW3123/00 curved Cu-filtered Cu-Kα (λ=1.54056) radiation. The samples were scanned in 2θ range of 2 to 80 degree at a scanning rate of 0.4 deg/s. Crystallite size of was determined from the characteristic peak (2θ = 38.5) for the (111) reflection using the Scherrer formula with a shape factor (K) of 0.9.

$$\text{Crystallite size} = K\lambda/W \cos\theta$$

Where, $W = W_b - W_s$, Wb is broadened profile width of experimental sample and W_s is standard profile width of reference sample. Fourier transform infrared spectra (FT-IR) were recorded using Perkin-Elmer-Spectrum GX- Spectrophotometer as KBr pellet. Particle sizes of Pd and Rh metal nanoparticles were determined from electron micrographs taken on *Philips CM 200 KeV* transmission electron microscope. One drop of dilute colloidal dispersion in propanol was placed on a formvar grid and allowed to stand for 30-40s. After solvent evaporation, electron micrographs were taken of the particles retained on the film. Particle sizes of gold and silver were determined from electron micrographs collected using Philips FEI's Tecnai F30 G2 300 KeV transmission electron microscope. One drop of dilute colloidal dispersion in toluene was placed on a 400 mesh copper grid. After solvent evaporation, electron micrographs were taken of the particles retained on the film. UV–vis DRS measurements were carried out at room temperature on a Varian Cary 500 instrument in the range of 400–700 nm. This setup was equipped with a diffuse reflectance accessory. The scan was made with an averaging time of 1 s, a data interval of 1 nm, and a scan rate of 60 nm/min. A baseline correction was performed using a dried barium sulfate white standard.

5.3. Results and Discussion (Pd and Rh Metal Nanoparticles Supported Organoclays)

5.3.1. FTIR and PXRD of Pd and Rh-MMT/Organoclay Hybrids

The FT-IR spectra of MMT and POMM are shown in Figure 5.3. The bands at 3620 and 3698cm^{-1} are due to -OH stretching mode of Al–OH and Si–OH of MMT structure. The broad band centered near 3400cm^{-1} is due to –OH stretching mode and overlaid absorption peaks in the region of 1640cm^{-1} is attributed to -OH bending mode of adsorbed water. The characteristic peak at 1115cm^{-1} is due to Si–O stretching, out-of-plane Si-O stretching mode for MMT. The formation of POMM is conformed by presence of the IR peaks at 2916 and 2854cm^{-1} are ascribed to the asymmetric and symmetric vibration of methylene groups $(CH_2)n$ of the aliphatic chain. In addition to this, there is also the HCH stretching vibration band at 1465cm^{-1} in IR spectrum. The IR absorption bands in the low frequency region of the MMT and partially organophilic MMT analogues were largely comparable indicating that the clay mineral matrix has not changed upon exchange of the interlayer ions by the quaternary ammonium ions.

The Pd and Rh nanoparticles generated on MMT, have agglomeration of metal nanoparticles. To overcome this problem, we have synthesized

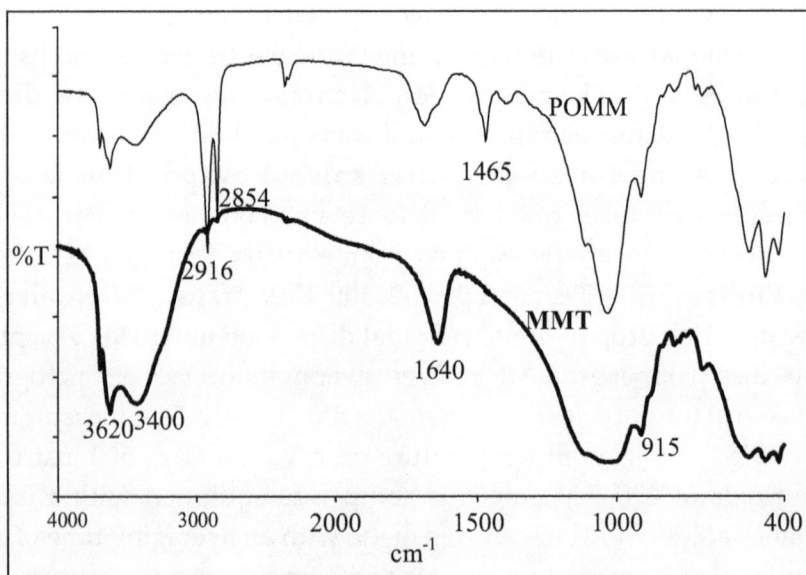

Figure 5.3. FT-IR spectra of virgin MMT and POMM.

POMM (HT 25, HT 50 and HT 75) and used these for supporting the metal nanoparticles. The organic modification is given in such a way that 75, 50 and 25 per cent of exchangeable cations are available (remain vacant) so that palladium tetraammine and rhodium hexaammine can be easily exchanged against interlayer cations. The formation of POMM is also confirmed by PXRD pattern as shown in Figure 5.4.

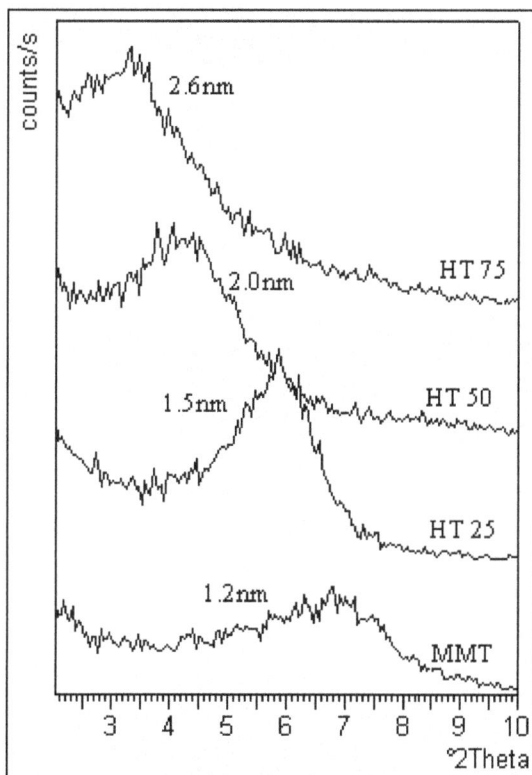

Figure 5.4. PXRD pattern of organoclay with different concentration of organic modifier and virgin MMT.

The interlayer arrangement of organic modifier in organophilic MMT is varying with the concentration of organic modifier. Bonczek *et al.*, had observed that long chain alkylammonium cations can conceivably adopt monolayer, bilayer, pseudotrimolecular, or paraffin-type arrangements depending on the charge density of the clay and the proportion of the CEC occupied [37]. The PXRD pattern of organoclay synthesized using different concentration of organic modifier (25 per cent, 50 per cent, and

75 per cent) and virgin MMT are shown in Figure 5.4. When 50 per cent or more long chain alkylammonium cations are exchanged against interlayer cations of MMT, the pseudotrimolecular or paraffin-type interlayer arrangements are observed. The interlayer arrangement of pseudotrimolecular and paraffin-type generates the cavities between 1nm thick alumino-silicate platelets, which acts as organophilic nano-phase reactor during the generation of Pd and Rh metal nanoparticles and helping to control the particle size of the Pd and Rh metal.

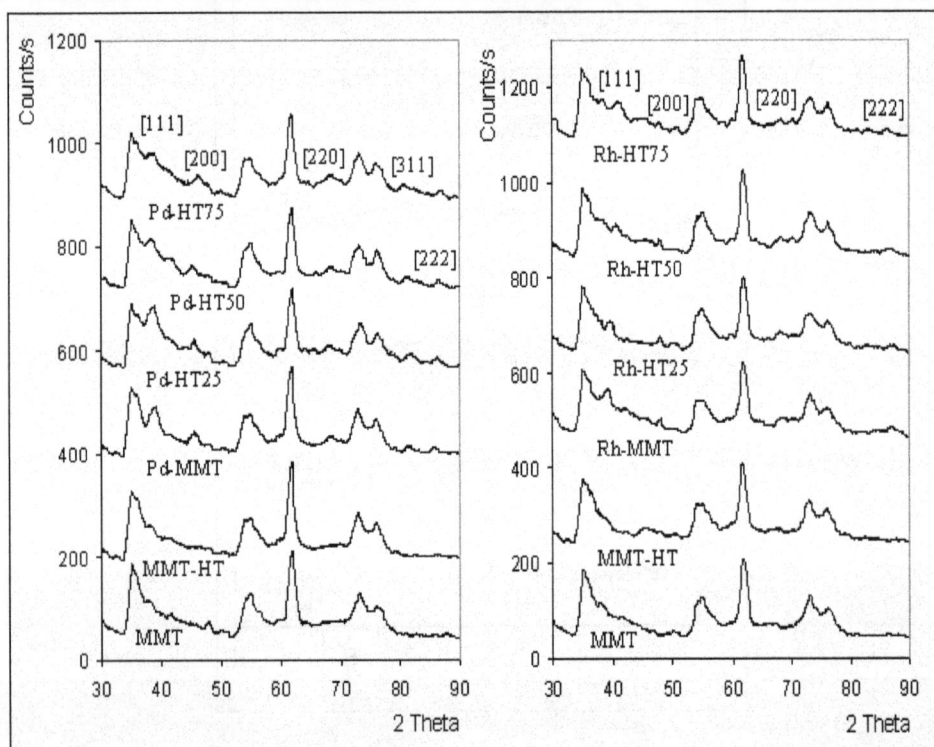

Figure 5.5. PXRD patterns of Pd and Rh supported MMT, HT 25, HT 50 and HT 75.

The PXRD pattern of Pd and Rh metal nanoparticles intercalated MMT and different POMM are shown in Figure 5.5. The characteristic peaks for Pd and Rh at the diffraction angles of 39°, 46°, 68°, 82°, and 86° correspond to the [111], [200], [220], [311] and [222] crystallographic planes of an fcc structure. The locations of the Bragg reflections are in accordance with those reported for the bulk state [38]. The relative intensity of the peaks are low in POMM supported Pd and Rh nanoparticle which is due to relatively lower amount of Pd and Rh metal on supporting materials. The crystallite size of the resulted Pd and Rh metal nanoparticle calculated from the characteristic peak ($2\theta = 39$) for the [111] using the Scherrer's formula [39] in Pd-MMT and Rh-MMT are 6.7 and 6.9 nm, in Pd - HT 25 and Rh - HT 25 are 5.6 and 6.1 nm, in Pd - HT 50 and Rh - HT 50 is 3.4 and 3.6 nm and in Pd - HT 75 and Rh - HT 75 is 3.3 and 3.6 nm respectively. These values suggest that the organic modification of MMT resulted into Pd and Rh metal with lower crystallite sizes. The interlayer spacing [001] of Pd-MMT, Rh-MMT, Pd - HT 50 and Rh - HT 50 is not affected so much rather than its intensity and width of the peak, which conformed that Pd and Rh metal nanoparticles are formed into interlayer spacing as well as on the surface of MMT and POMM. The metal nanoparticles formed on the external surface of the virgin MMT are expected to be more as compared to POMM due to the lower interlayer spacing of MMT. On the other hand, in case of POMM, the metal nanoparticles are likely to form in the interlayer spacing due to its higher interlayer spacing and smaller metal particle size.

5.3.2. TEM Analysis of Pd and Rh-MMT/Organoclay Hybrids

The TEM images and particle size distribution patterns are shown in Figure 5.6 and 5.7. The average particle size of Pd in Pd-MMT, Rh in Rh-MMT, Pd in Pd - HT 50 and Rh - HT 50 is 20 nm, 25 nm, 8 nm and 13 nm respectively (Table 5.1). This clearly indicates that the organic modification of MMT greatly reduced the particle size of Pd and Rh metal nanoparticles. The organic modification of MMT also affects the dispersion of metal nanoparticles, with pre-organic modification nearly mono dispersed metal nanoparticles are obtained.

The TEM images of Pd-MMT and Rh-MMT (Figure 5.6) clearly reveals the agglomeration of Pd and Rh metal particles. Because of absence of organic modifier to control the size of metal particles during reduction, resulted into agglomeration of particles. In case of Pd - HT 50 and Rh - HT 50 as shown in Figure 5.7, the fine dispersion of Pd and Rh nanoparticles thought out supported material are observed.

This is due to presence of organic phase which acts as a particle size controlling agent by forming organophilic cavities within the MMT (nano-phase reactor) which clearly emphasize that the mean size of the metal

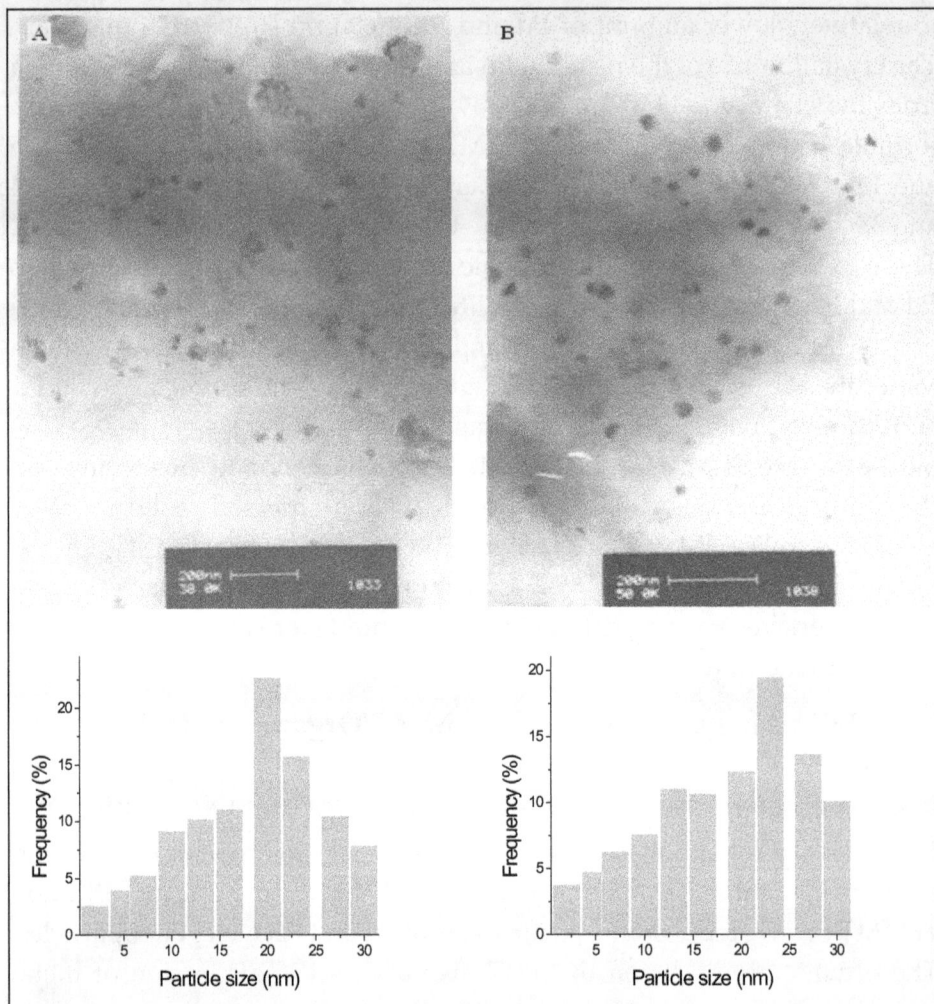

Figure 5.6. TEM images and particle size distribution patterns of Pd-MMT (A), and Rh-MMT (B), Scale 200 nm.

particles and the metal loading in MMT and POMM are interrelated. Moreover, the control over the particle size with the extent of pre-organic modification is also closely related to the surface site density of the precursor compound; smaller particle size is associated with lower particle loadings (as a consequence of low precursor concentration on the surface), and larger particle size is accompanied by higher particle loadings.

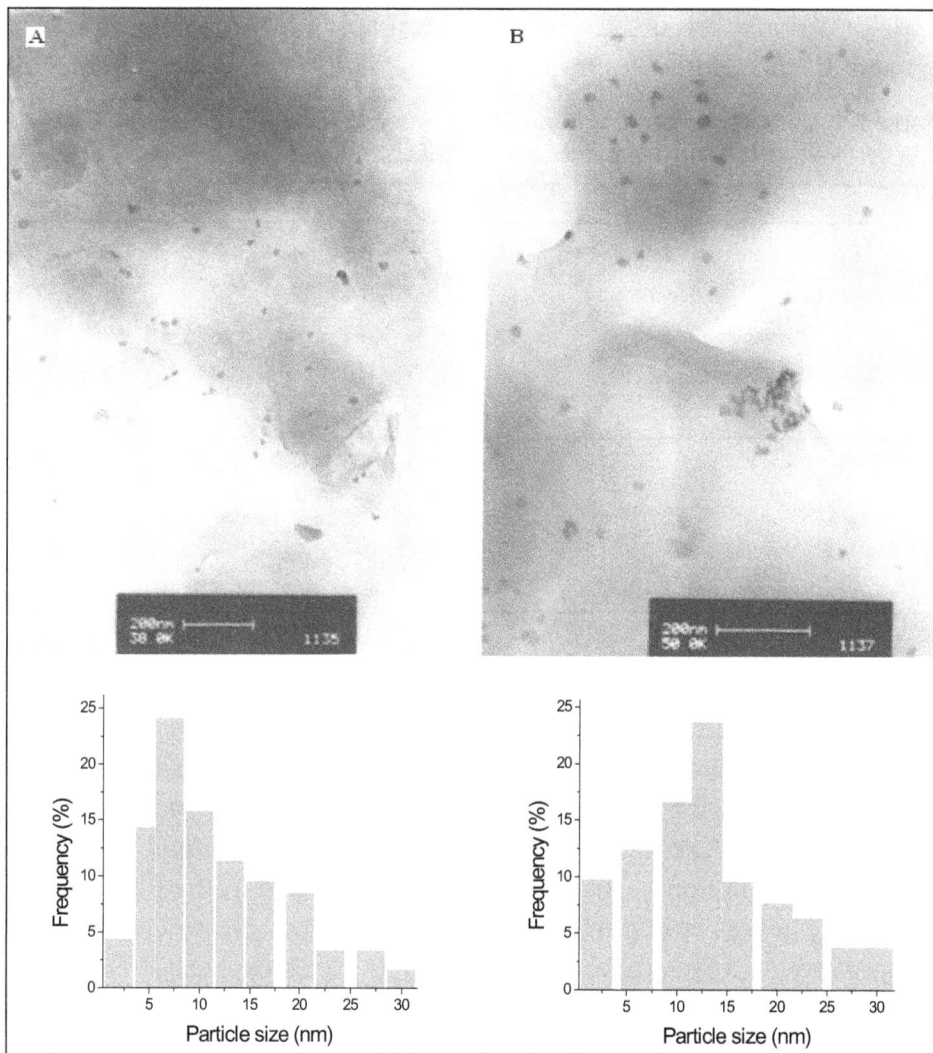

Figure 5.7. TEM images and particle size distribution patterns of Pd – HT 50(A), and Rh – HT 50(B), Scale 200 nm.

The Pd and Rh nanoparticles supported on MMT and POMM synthesized by this technique resulted into almost theoretical amount of Pd and Rh. The loading Pd and Rh cationic precursor is depending on the CEC of the MMT and POMM. This is also the advantage of this novel technique to minimize the loss of metal nanoparticle during synthesis, because the subsequent reduction was carried out after interacting Pd and Rh cationic precursor. The theoretical and experimental amount of Pd and Rh (per cent w/w) measured by ICP-AES is reported in Table 5.1.

Table 5.1. Comparison of theoretical and experimental content, average particle and crystallite size of palladium and rhodium in MMT and POMM.

		Pd-MMT	*Pd – HT 25*	*Pd –HT 50*	*Pd – HT 75*
Pd	Theoretical	9.6	8.3	4.3	2.1
per cent w/w	Experimental	9.4	8.1	4.2	1.8
d_{Pd}, nm (TEM)		20 ± 3	–	8 ± 2	–
Crystallite size (nm; XRD)		6.7	5.6	3.4	3.3
		Rh - MMT	*Rh – HT 25*	*Rh –HT 50*	*Rh – HT 75*
Rh	Theoretical	2.9	2.2	1.4	0.7
per cent w/w	Experimental	2.7	2.2	1.1	0.6
d_{Rh}, nm (TEM)		25 ± 3	–	13 ± 2	–
Crystallite size (nm; XRD)		6.9	6.1	3.6	3.6

5.4. Results and Discussion (Au and Ag Metal Nanoparticles Anchored Organoclays)

During synthesis of nanoparticles using Path 1, the $HAuCl_4$ or $AgNO_3$ salt is situated in the internal part of the micelles formed in the aqueous solution of HDTA or DODA surfactant. Addition of an aqueous sodium borohydride solution to the micellar system resulted in the formation of Au or Ag metal nanoparticles, stabilized by the cationic surfactant molecules which are adsorbed on the surface of nanoparticles. Therefore, the stabilizing effect of the surfactant molecules prevented the aggregation of nanosized Au or Ag nanoclusters. Quaternary ammonium salts are known to form micelles in aqueous solution. The critical micelle concentration for HDTA is 10 µM and varies from 1 mM for n = 10 to 10 µM for n = 16 (n indicates number of carbon atom in the surfactant alkyl chain) [40]. We have synthesized Au nanoparticles in 0.5 mM aqueous solution of surfactant. However, there could be some effect on the micelle formation both for HDTA and DODA in the presence of $HAuCl_4$ or $AgNO_3$ salt in aqueous solution at temperature of 80 °C. Moreover, the DODA, a surfactant with two long alkyl chains form different micelles in the presence of ionic substances and varies with temperature than that in pure water.

The phenomenon is different when the Au or Ag nanoparticles are synthesized in organoclay using Path 2, where nucleation and growth of Au or Ag nanoparticles are within the molecular arrangement of alkyl ammonium cation attached through ionic bonding to the positively charged alumino-silicate sheets. The basal spacing [001] for MHDT and MDOD is 1.8 and 2.9 nm, suggesting that the formation of bilayer and tilted-paraffin type arrangement of quaternary ammonium cation within MMT. Thus, in synthetic methodology using Path 2, $HAuCl_4$ or $AgNO_3$ salt is situated randomly within bilayer arrangement of hexadecyltrimethylammonium cation or tilted arrangement of dioctadecyldimethylammonium cation attached to MMT surfaces. Subsequent reduction results into Au or Ag nanoparticles stabilized by organophilic cavities generated by alkyl chains within alumino-silicate platelets. In this case, the organophilic cavities as well as alumino-silicate platelets acts as nano-phase reactor and control the nucleation-growth processes, which leads to formation Au or Ag nanoclusters.

5.4.1. PXRD Study of Au and Ag – Organoclays Hybrids

The characteristic peaks for Au or Ag at the diffraction angles of 38.5°, 44.5°, 64.5°, and 78° correspond to the [111], [200], [220] and [311] crystallographic planes as shown in Figure 5.8. The other reflections observed in PXRD pattern correspond to the structure of MMT with dominant reflection to [001] for basal spacing. The characteristic reflections for Au and Ag are broader in the samples with lower concentration of Au or Ag nanoparticles, suggesting the presence of nanosized Au or Ag particles. Furthermore the intensity for the samples (~1 per cent w/w Au or Ag anchored on organoclay) is low as compared to organoclay containing higher concentration (~ 5 per cent w/w) of Au and Ag clusters (M5HDTG and M5HDTS). The values of basal spacing of Au or Ag-organoclay hybrids are tabulated in Table 5.2.

The crystallite size of the resulted Au or Ag nanoparticles are calculated from the characteristic peak (2θ = 38.5°) for the reflection [111] using the Scherrer's formula. It is observed that the Au and Ag crystallite of small size are formed in Au or Ag-organoclay containing surfactant with two long alkyl chains as compared to the surfactant with only single long alkyl chain. The crystallite size of Au nanoparticles varies from 1.7 to 2.6 nm whereas for Ag nanoparticles, 1.8 to 3.4 nm as shown in Table 5.2.

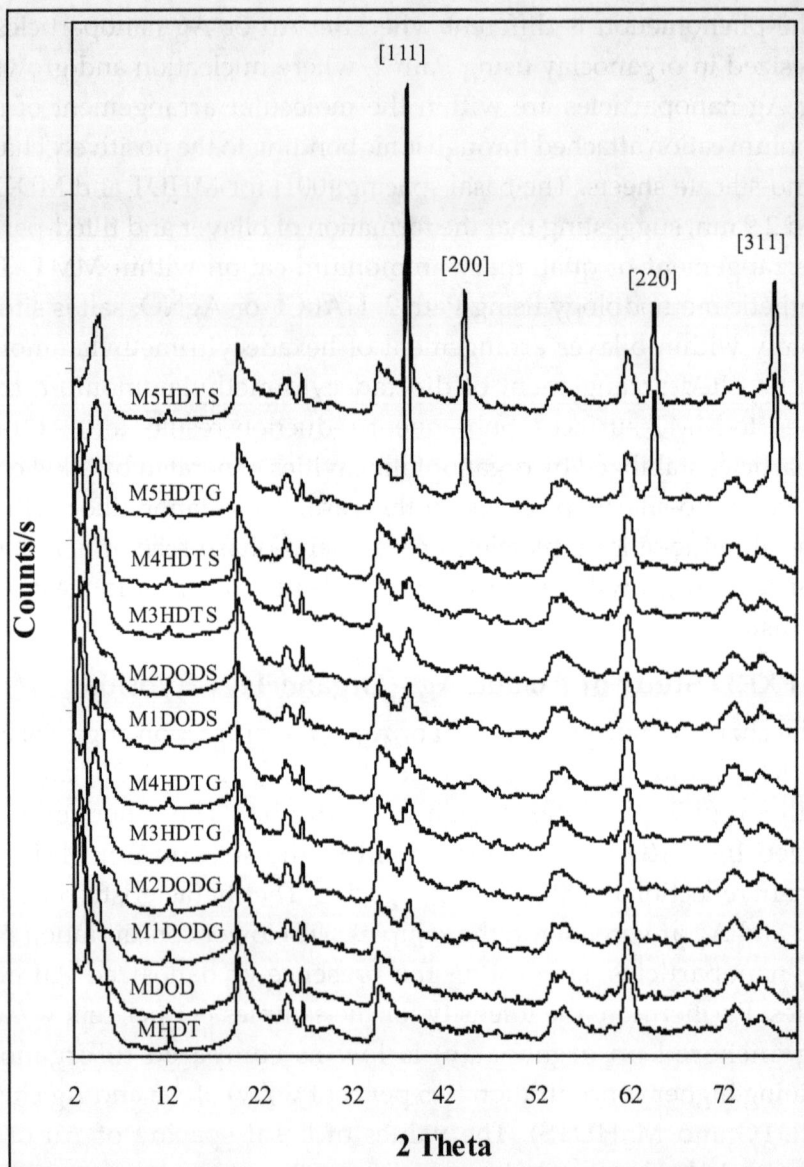

Figure 5.8. PXRD pattern of organoclay and Au or Ag nanoparticles anchored organoclays.

The higher concentration of Au or Ag nanoparticles leads to intense PXRD reflections with substantial increase in the crystallite size. The crystallite size of Au (M5HDTG) and Ag (M5HDTS) are observed to be 18.3 and 21.1 nm, respectively. The basal spacing of MHDT and MDOD are 1.8

and 2.9 nm. After the intercalation of Au or Ag nanoparticles, there is slight difference in the basal spacing of Au or Ag - organoclay hybrids compared to pristine organoclay. The crystallite size calculated by PXRD and particle size observed by TEM are higher than the interlayer spacing of organoclay. However, the peak intensity and broadness of the [001] reflections suggests that the Au or Ag nanoparticles with very fine particles are formed within the layers of the organoclays. Thus, it is proposed that the Au or Ag nanoparticles are formed on both the surface and interlayer space of organoclays.

Table 5.2. Basal spacing, crystallite size, particle size, and Au and Ag content of hybrids.

Samples	M1DODG	M2DODG	M3HDTG	M4HDTG	M5HDTG
Basal spacing, nm	3.1	3.3	1.9	1.9	1.9
Crystallite size, nm	1.7	1.4	2.6	2.3	18.3
Particle size, d_{nm}	5.34	3.68	5.72	4.03	26.35
Au content, per cent w/w	0.88	0.87	0.96	1.03	5.12
	M1DODS	M2DODS	M3HDTS	M4HDTS	M5HDTS
Crystallite size, nm	2.1	1.8	3.4	3.1	21.3
Particle size, d_{nm}	6.03	5.38	6.51	5.25	33.06
Ag content, per cent w/w	0.92	0.97	1.1	1.04	4.86

#: Basal spacing of MHDT and MDOD are 1.8 and 2.9 nm respectively.

5.4.2. TEM Analysis of Au and Ag – Organoclays Hybrids

The evidence of the formation of Au and Ag nanoparticles is confirmed by the transmission electron micrographs (TEM) as shown in Figures 5.9-5.12. TEM measurements and observations on gold and silver nanoparticles intercalated organoclays were carried out at low and high magnification. Spherically shaped single nanoparticles of Au and Ag are observed. The Au and Ag nanoparticles are in most cases well separated, however, some cluster aggregation has been observed on the surface of the organoclays in the case of gold and silver nanoparticles synthesized by path 2. Figure 5.9 shows TEM micrograph and the corresponding size distribution of Au-organoclay hybrids synthesized by path 1 and 2. The inset in the Figure is the selected area electron diffraction (SAED) pattern and HRTEM image of one of the gold nanoparticles. SAED demonstrates

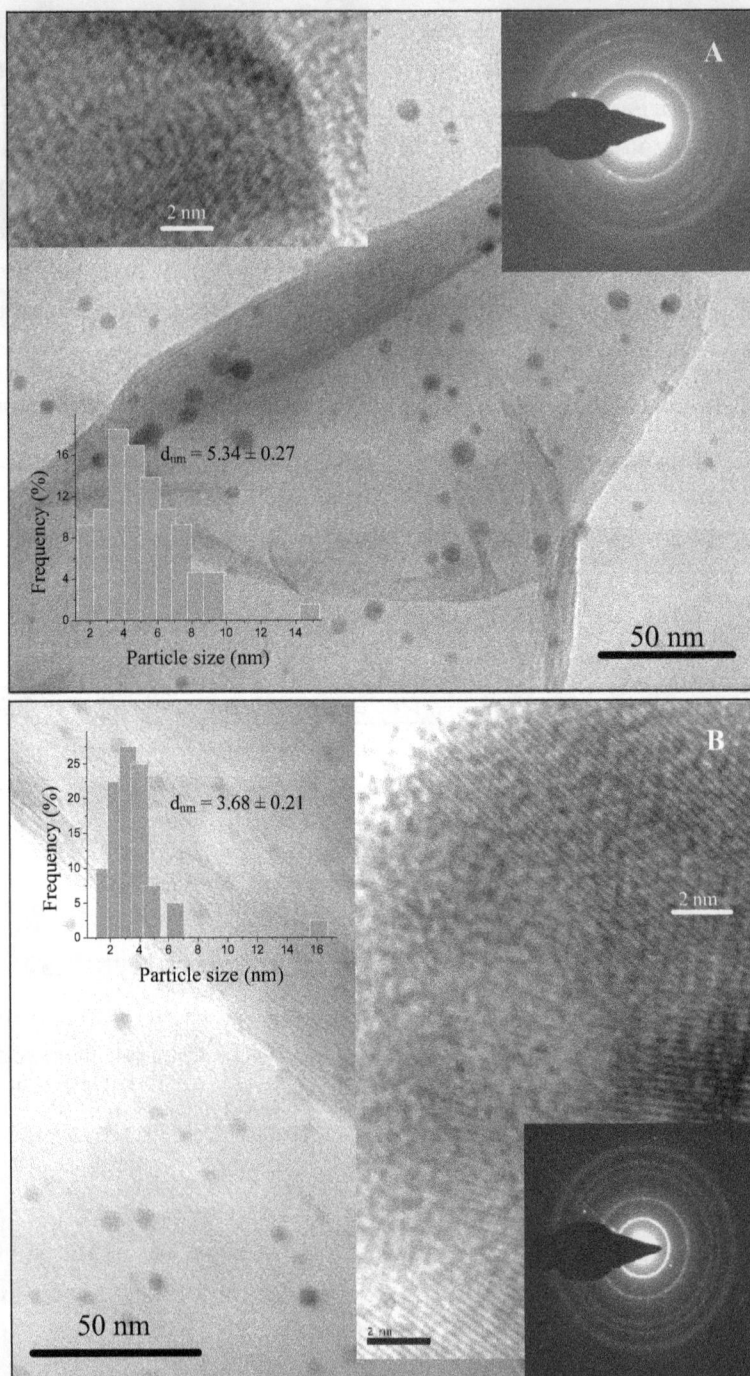

Figure 5.9. TEM images of Au nanoparticles anchored organoclay synthesized by (A) path 1; M1DODG (B) path 2; M2DODG (inset figure shows HRTEM image, SAED and particle size distribution).

diffraction spots, which also proves crystalline characteristic of Au nanoparticles. The lattice planes in the gold nanoparticles can be clearly seen and [111] lattice spacing is 0.233 nm. The average particle size of Au nanoparticles as determined by TEM in M1DODG and M2DODG are 5.34 and 3.68 nm, respectively. The narrow particle size distribution is observed when the Au nanoparticles were synthesized by path 2. It is clearly seen from the Figure 5.9 B that the finer particles are situated at the interlayer spacing of the organoclay. Figure 5.10 A, B shows Au nanoparticles synthesized using hexadecyltrimethylammonium cation by both the paths. From these Figures, it is observed that Au nanoparticles synthesized by path 1 resulted into broader particle size distribution. The average particle size of Au nanoparticles in M2HDTG and M3HDTG are 6.03 and 5.72 nm, respectively.

The finer particles of Au are formed using surfactant with two long alkyl chains (M1DODG and M2DODG) than a surfactant with single alkyl chain in case of M3HDTG and M4HDTG. It is clearly seen that most of the Au nanoparticles are spherical in shape and well separated from each other.

The particle sizes of the Ag nanoparticles are within a range of 4.03 to 6.51 nm in all the samples and particle distributions are uneven, probably due to formation of AgCl or AgBr in quaternary ammonium salts during the synthesis. The particle size is higher than that of Au nanoparticles synthesized using the same surfactants and the same method. Figure 5.11 and 5.12 shows the TEM image of the Ag nanoparticles anchored organoclay synthesized using DODA and HDTA, respectively. The average particle size of Ag nanoparticles in M1DODS and M2DODS are 5.38 and 4.03 nm, respectively. Inset Figure shows HRTEM image and SAED recorded from the Ag nanoparticles along with the particle size distribution pattern. The lattice planes in the Ag nanoparticles can be clearly seen with a lattice spacing of 0.229 nm. The diffraction rings with intense spots are due to fcc Ag unit cell structure with high crystallinity. It can be clearly seen from the Figure 5.11 B and 5.12 B that the agglomeration of the Ag nanoparticles on the surface of the organoclays is observed. The average particle size of Ag nanoparticles in M3HDTS and M4HDTS are 6.51 and 5.25 nm, respectively. The Au or Ag nanoparticles are reasonably monodispersed at low concentration of Au or Ag.

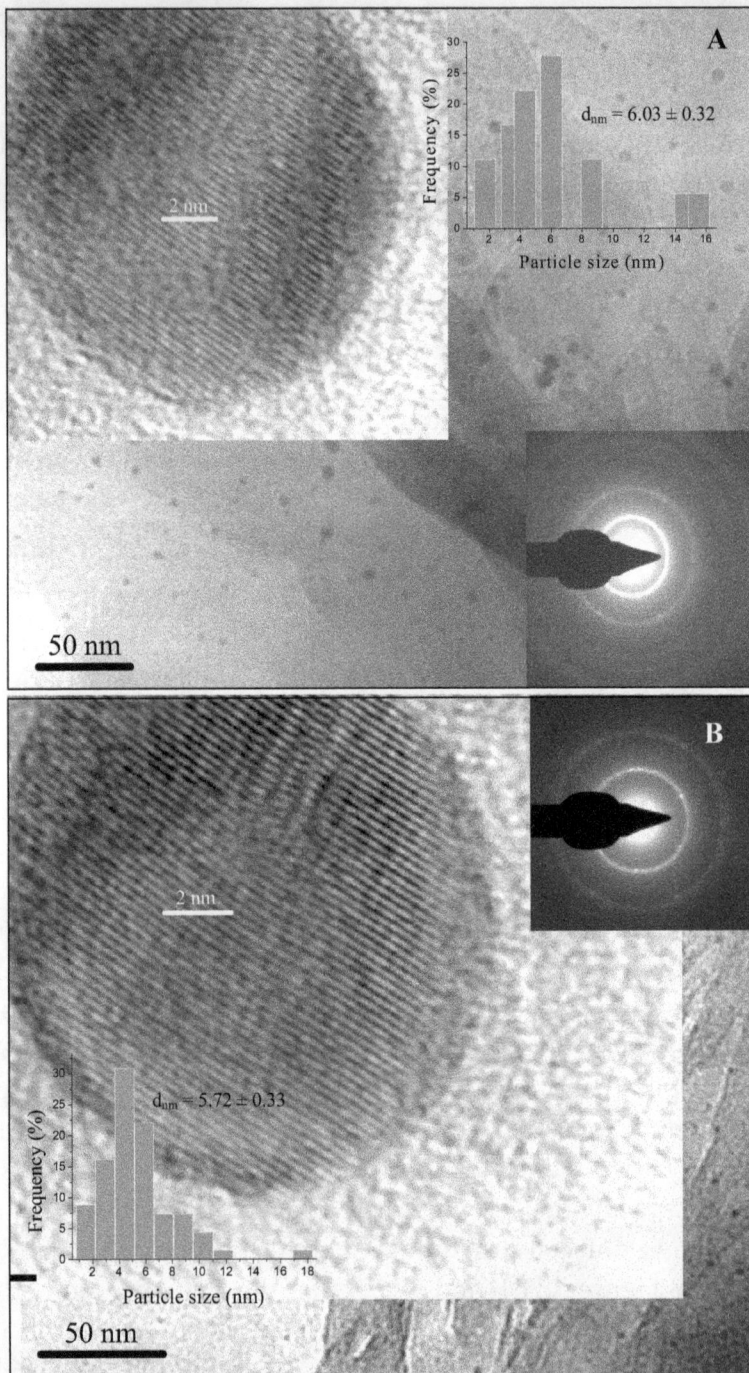

Figure 5.10. TEM images of Au nanoparticles anchored organoclay synthesized by (A) path 1; M3HDTG (B) path 2; M4HDTG (inset figure shows HRTEM image, SAED and particle size distribution).

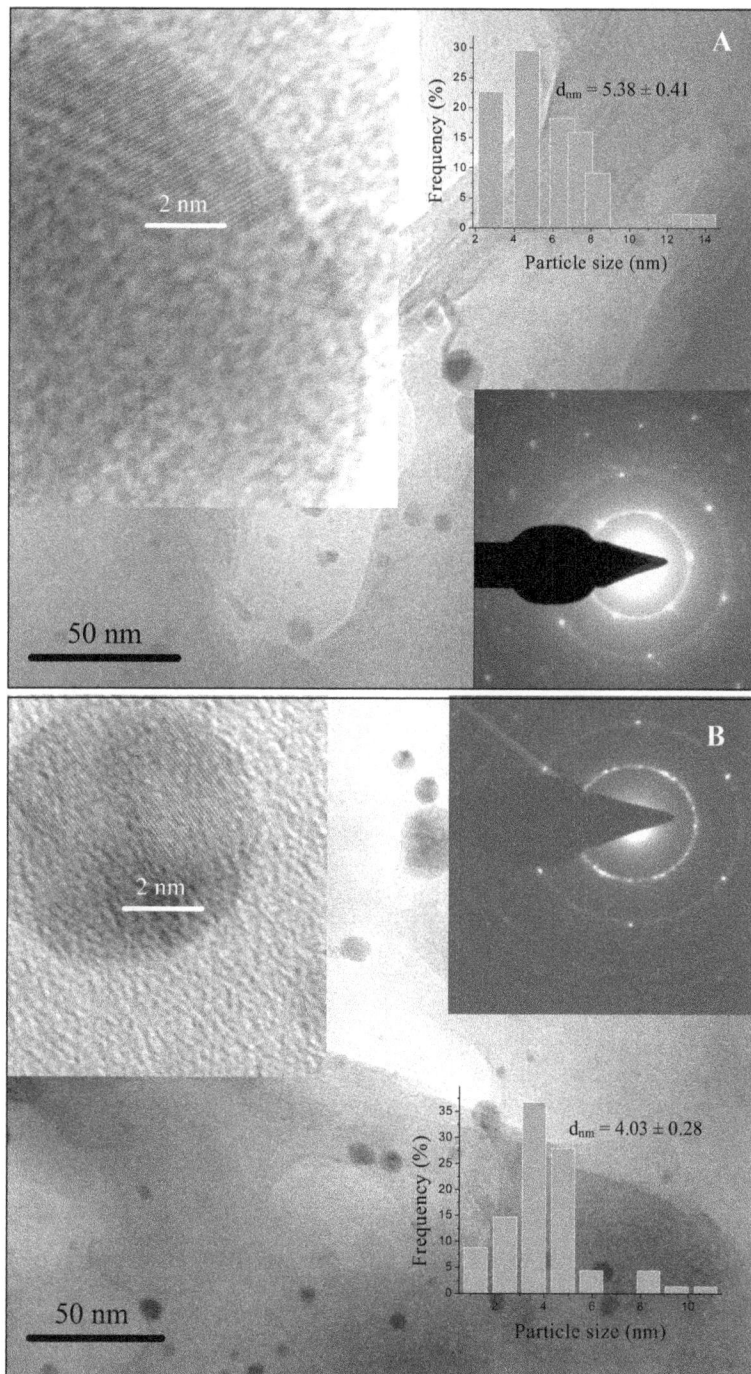

Figure 5.11. TEM images of Ag nanoparticles anchored organoclay synthesized by (A) path 1; M1DODS (B) path 2; M2DODS (inset figure shows HRTEM image, SAED and particle size distribution).

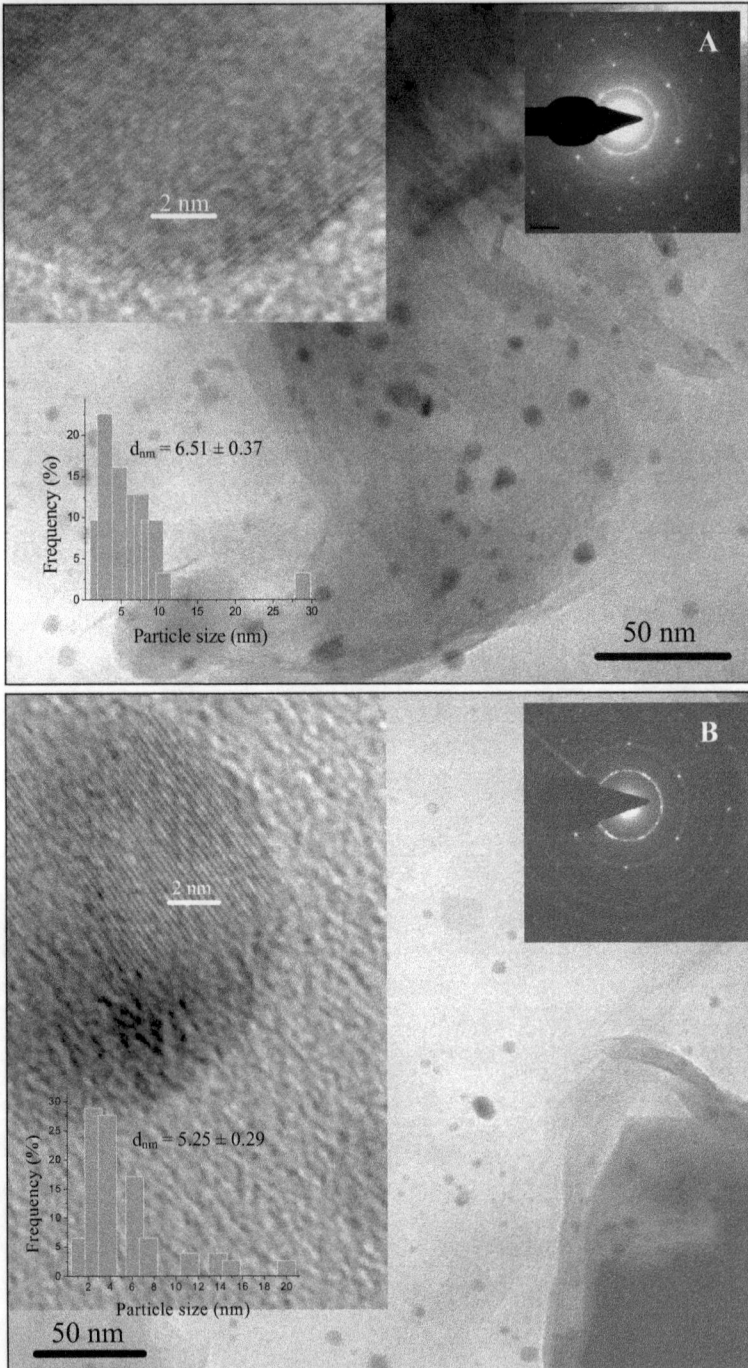

Figure 5.12. TEM images of Ag nanoparticles anchored organoclay synthesized by (A) path 1; M3HDTS (B) path 2; M4HDTS (inset figure shows HRTEM image, SAED and particle size distribution).

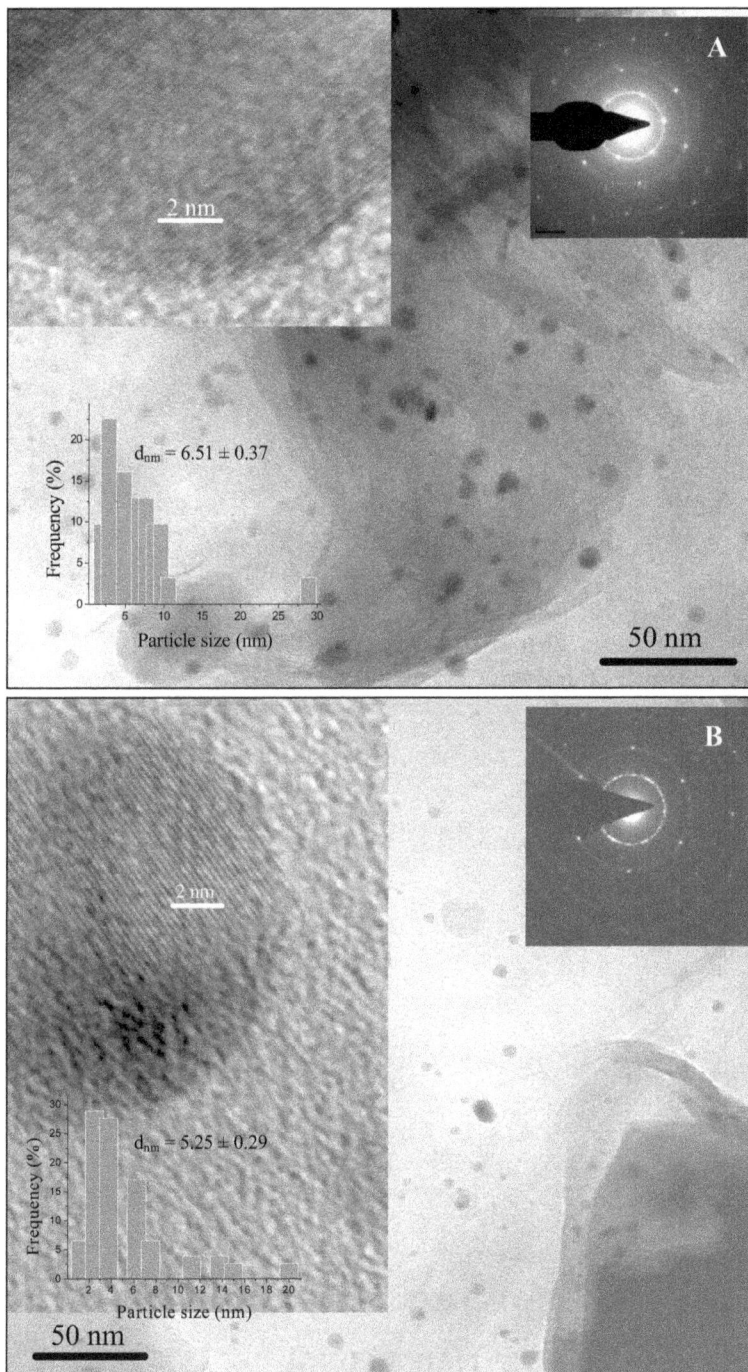

Figure 5.13. TEM images of Au (M5HDTG) Ag (M5HDTS) nanoparticles anchored organoclay synthesized by path 1 (inset figure shows SAED and particle size distribution).

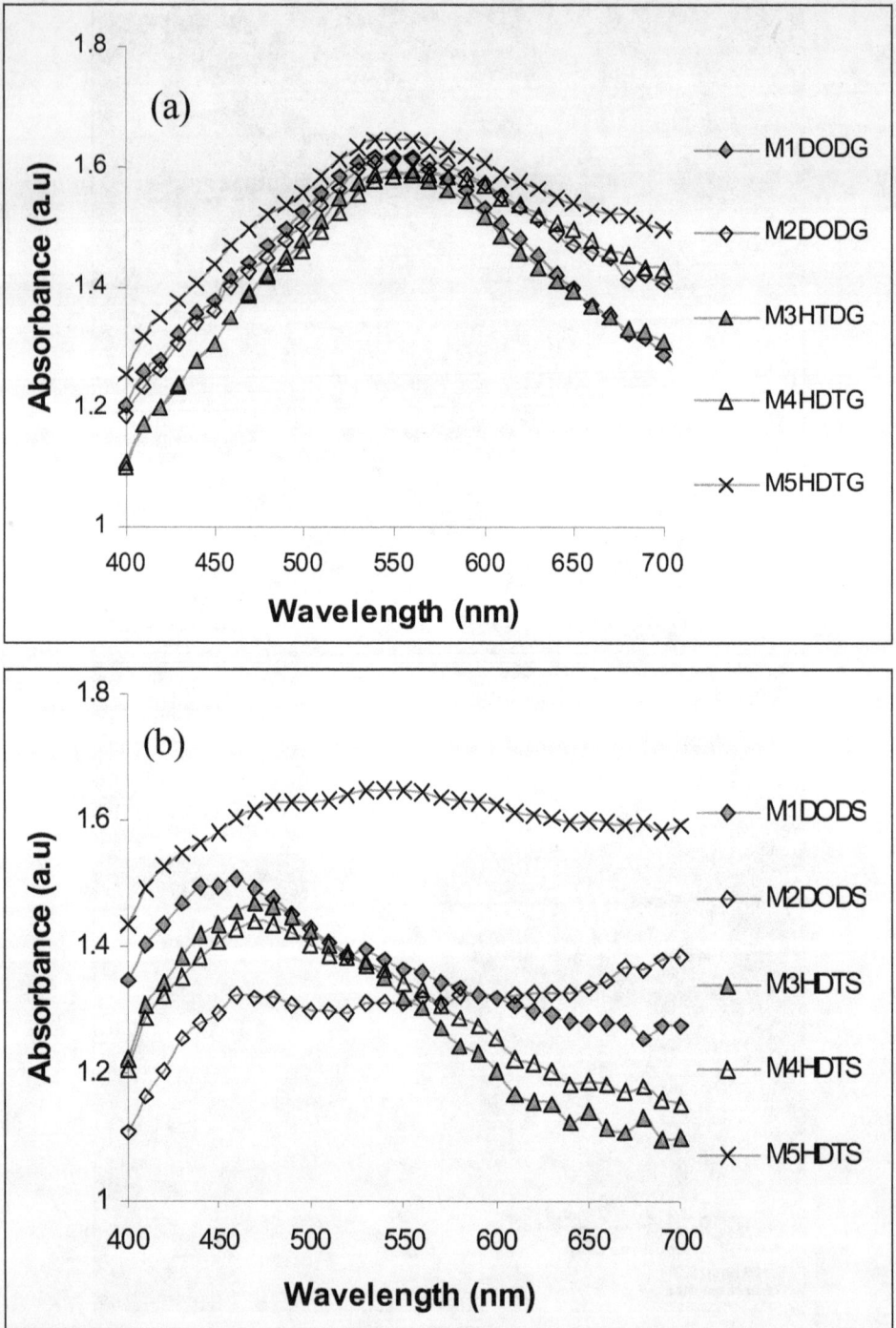

Figure 5.14. Diffuse reflectance UV-visible spectra of (a) Au-organoclay and (b) Ag-organoclay hybrids.

It was observed that the particle size increased with increasing Au and Ag content and favored the formation of larger, more crystalline and polydispersed nanoparticles. The average particle size of Au and Ag nanoparticles in M5HDTG and M5HDTS are 26.35 and 33.06 nm, respectively. The TEM images with respective SAED and particle size distribution of M5HDTG and M5HDTS are shown in Figure 5.13.

From the diffuse reflectance UV-vis spectra as shown in Figure 5.14, it is observed that Au-organoclay hybrids attained a wine red (for lower concentration of Au) color and purple (for higher concentration of Au) color typical of the presence of Au nanoparticles. These materials had a characteristic absorption band in the visible region of the electromagnetic spectrum at around 520-550 nm. The color of Ag-organoclay hybrids with lower concentration of Ag nanoparticles observed to be yellow whereas with higher concentration of Ag nanoparticles resulted yellowish green. The characteristic absorption band at around 420-470 nm obtained for Ag nanoparticles supported on solid matrix. The observed absorption bands are due to surface plasmon vibrations, which are dependent on the gold particle size and the supporting clay [41-43].

References

1. Daniel M. C. and Astruc D., *Chem. Rev.*, 104, 293, 2004.

2. Rao C. N. R., Kulkarni G. U., Thomas P. J. and Edwards P. P., *Chem. Soc. Rev.*, 29, 27, 2000.

3. Capek I., *Adv. Collo. Inter. Sci.*, 110, 49, 2004.

4. Dekany I., Turi L. and Kiraly Z., *Appl. Clay Sci.*, 15, 221, 1999.

5. Kiraly Z., Dekany I., Mastalir A. and Bartoky M., *J. Catal.*, 161, 401, 1996.

6. Papp Sz., Szucs A. and Dekany I., *Solid State Ionics*, 141-142, 169, 2001.

7. Papp Sz. and Dekany I., *Collo. Polym. Sci.*, 280, 956, 2002.

8. Berkovich Y. and Garti N., *Coll. Surf. A.*, 128, 91, 1997.

9. Mayer A. B. R. and Mark J. E., *Coll. Polym. Sci.*, 275, 333, 1997.

10. Esumi K., Suzuki A., Aihara N., Usui K. and Toringoe K., *Langmuir*, 14, 3157, 1998.

11. Yonezawa T. and Toshima N., *J. Mol. Catal.*, 83, 167, 1993.

12. Kiraly Z., Veisz B., Mastalir A., Razgac Z. and Dekany I., *Chem. Commun.*, 1925, 1999.

13. Kiraly Z., Veisz B., Mastalir A. and Kofarago Gy., *Langmuir*, 17, 5381, 2001.

14. Szucs A., Bergera F. and Dekany I., *Collo. Surf. A.*, 174, 387, 2000.

15. Papp Sz., Szel J., Oszko A. and Dekany I., *Chem. Mater.*, 16, 1674, 2004.

16. Papp Sz. and Dekany I., *Prog. Collo. Poly. Sci.*, 117, 94, 2001.

17. Jhung S. H., Lee J. H., Lee J. M., Lee J. H., Hong D. Y, Kim M. W. and Chang J. S., *Bull. Korean Chem. Soc.*, 26(4), 563, 2005.

18. Yoon B. and Wai C. M., *J. Am. Chem. Soc.*, 127, 17174, 2005.

19. Gommes C. J., Jong K., Pirard J. P. and Blacher S., *Langmuir*, 21, 12378, 2005.

20. Schulz P. G., Gonzalez M. G., Quincoces C. E. and Gigola C. E., *Ind. Eng. Chem. Res.*, 44, 9020, 2005.

21. Miyamura H., Matsubara R., Miyazaki Y. and Kobayashi S., *Angew. Chem. Int. Ed.*, 46, 4151, 2007.

22. Mallat T. and Baiker A., *Chem. Rev.*, 104, 3037, 2004.

23. Bamwenda G. R., Obuchi A., Ogata A., Oi J., Kushiyama S. and Mizuno K., *J. Mol. Catal. A: Chem.*, 126, 151, 1997.

24. Idakiev V., Tabakova T., Andreev A. and Giovanoli R., *Appl. Catal. A: Gen.*, 134, 275, 1996.

25. Sau T. K. and Murphy C. J., *J. Am. Chem. Soc.*, 126, 8648, 2004.

26. Prati L. and Rossi M., *J. Catal.*, 176, 552, 1998.

27. Murphy C. J. and Jana N. R., *Adv. Mater.*, 14, 80, 2002.

28. Gou L. and Murphy C. J., *Chem. Mater.*, 17, 3668, 2005.

29. Yan W., Mahurin S. M., Chen B., Overbury S. H. and Dai S., *J. Phys. Chem. B*, 109, 15489, 2005.

30. Carrettin S., McMorn P., Johnston P., Griffin Ken., Kiely C. J. and Hutchings G. *J. Phys. Chem. Chem. Phys.*, 5, 1329, 2003.

31. Aihara N., Torigoe K. and Esumi K., *Langmuir*, 14, 4945, 1998.

32. Paek S.-M., Jang J.-U., Hwang S.-J. and Choy J.-H., *J. Phys. Chem. Solids*, 67, 1020, 2006.

33. Chen C.-C. and Kuo P.-L., *J. Collo. Inter. Sci.*, 293, 101, 2006.

34. Aihara N., Torigoe K. and Esumi, K., *Langmuir*, 14, 4945, 1998.

35. Bailar J. C., 1953. Inorganic Syntheses, *McGraw-Hill*, USA, Vol. 4, p180.

36. Patel H. A., Somani R. S., Bajaj H. C. and Jasra R. V., *Appl. Clay Sci.*, 35, 194, 2007.

37. Bonczek J. L., Harris W. G. and Nkedi-Kizza P., *Clays Clay Miner.*, 50(1), 11, 2002.

38. Veisz B., Kiraly Z., Toth L. and Pecz B., *Chem. Mater.*, 14, 2882, 2002.

39. Mishra M. K., Tyagi B. and Jasra R. V., *Ind. Eng. Chem. Res.*, 42, 5727, 2003.

40. Gao J., Bender C. M. and Murphy C. J., *Langmuir*, 19, 9065, 2003.

41. Sacaliuc E., Beale A. M., Weckhuysen B. M. and Nijhuis T. A., *J. Catal.*, 248, 235, 2007.

42. Tuzovskaya I., Bogdanchikova N., Simakov A., Gurin V., Pestryakov A., Avalos M. and Farýas M. H., *Chem. Phys.*, 338, 23, 2007.

43. Jena B. K. and Retna Raj C., *Langmuir*, 23, 4064, 2007.

Chapter 6
Adsorption of Aqueous Nitrobenzene on Organoclays

6.1. Introduction

Removal of organic pollutants from contaminated wastewater is critical to ensuring the safety of water supplies worldwide. Nitroaromatic compounds are widely used as pesticides, explosives, solvents, and intermediates in the synthesis of dyes, plastics and other chemicals [1-2]. Nitrobenzene has been nominated by the National Institute of Environmental Health Sciences for listing in the report on carcinogens based on the conclusions of an International Agency for Research on Cancer (IARC). The U.S. Environmental Protection Agency (EPA) recommends that levels in lakes and streams should be limited to 17 parts of nitrobenzene per million parts of water (17 ppm) to prevent possible health effects from drinking water or eating fish contaminated with nitrobenzene [3]. The U. S. Occupational Safety and Health Administration (OSHA) has set a permissible exposure limit of 5 mg of nitrobenzene per cubic meter of air for an 8 h workday in a 40 h work week [3]. A small amount of nitrobenzene can cause mild irritation if it contacts the skin or eyes directly. However, repeated exposures to a high concentration of nitrobenzene can result in methemoglobinemia, a condition in which the blood's ability to carry oxygen is reduced. It has been estimated that about 19 million pounds of nitrobenzene is released into the environment annually [4]. Nitrobenzene is released into the environment mainly by industries, but it can also form in the atmosphere through the nitration of benzene, a common air pollutant. However, the largest source of nitrobenzene release is its manufacture and use as a chemical intermediate in the synthesis of aniline. Smaller amounts are also released from consumer a product in which nitrobenzene is used as a solvent. The highest concentration of nitrobenzene is reported in wastewater from the organics and plastics industries, with some reported levels exceeding 100ppm [4].

Therefore, a variety of wastewater treatment technologies such as adsorption, ozonation and advanced oxidation processes have been employed for the purification of nitrobenzene contaminated water. Activated carbon served as most efficient adsorbent for nitrobenzene adsorption. However, activated carbon is flammable and difficult to regenerate [5]. Thus, alternative adsorbent for nitrobenzene removal is required. Adsorption of organic contaminants from water on different layered and porous inorganic materials and its organic derivatives have been used for years [6-7]. Recent development of photocatalytic degradation of organic contaminants in wastewater using TiO_2 as photocatalyst has also been the thrust area for tackling environmental problems [8]. In aqueous systems, water is intercalated into the inter-lamellar space of the montmorillonite (MMT) due to hydration of inorganic cations on the exchange site, resulting in expansion of the MMT. Adsorption of nonionic organic solutes from water to bentonite is relatively weak because of the preferential attraction of polar water molecules to the polar mineral surfaces. Thus, MMT is ineffective sorbents for non ionic organic compounds in the presence of water. Organic derivatives of MMT (organoclay) with different types of organic modifiers are more effective than their unmodified counterparts in the sorption of organic contaminants from water. Organoclay sorbs organic contaminants through adsorption or partitioning phenomenon, depending on the structure of the organic cation that has been exchanged on the MMT and type of organic contaminants (polar or nonpolar) present in the wastewater [9-11].

Boyd *et al.*, [12] reported adsorption mechanism of various substituted nitrobenzene on K^+, Na^+, Mg^{+2}, Ca^{+2} and Ba^{+2} exchanged smectite clay and concluded that the potential for adsorption of substituted nitrobenzene by K^+-smectite is determined largely by the additive interactions of the -NO_2 groups and the secondary substituent with interlayer K^+ ions. Zhu *et al.*, [13-14] have described that the sorption of polar organic contaminants onto organoclays resulted nonlinear isotherm, mainly governed by adsorption and other specific interaction while sorption of nonpolar contaminants followed partition phenomenon. Farkas A. *et al.*, [15] have studied arrangement of nitrobenzene in the interlayer space of the hexadecylpyridinium-MMT, resulted monolayer at low concentration of pollutant by replacing water molecules and bilayer orientation with the alkyl chain solvated by the pollutant. Pernyeszi *et al.*, [16] have studied the adsorption of 2,4-dichlorophenol on organoclay/aquifer materials in static and flow conditions.

In this chapter, we have illustrated the detailed study on the sorption of aqueous nitrobenzene solution on organoclay in a batch and fixed-bed sorption system. The effect of size of sorbent, flow rate of sorbate solution, temperature of the sorption, concentration of sorbate and sorbent with different amount of organic modifier exchanged in MMT on breakthrough curves. Desorption of nitrobenzene from organoclay in fixed-bed is also studied. Moreover, the important column parameters such as time for primary sorption zone to move up its length (t_z), total time involved for establishment of primary sorption zone (t_E), rate at which the exchange zone is moving up through the bed (U_z), fractional capacity (F), the height of the exchange zone (h_z), percentage of the total column saturated at breakthrough (per cent S) and breakthrough capacity are calculated on the basis of breakthrough.

6.2. Experimental Section

6.2.1. Materials

Bentonite lumps were collected from Barmer district of Rajasthan, India. Hexadecyl trimethylammonium bromide: $CH_3(CH_2)_{15}N(CH_3)_3 \cdot Br$, Stearyldimethylbenzylammonium chloride: $C_6H_5CH_2N[(CH_2)_{17}CH_3]$ $(CH_3)_2 \cdot Cl$, Dioctadecyldimethylammonium chloride $[(CH_2)_{17}CH_3]_2N$ $(CH_3)_2 \cdot Cl$ were purchased from Sigma-Aldrich, USA. Nitrobenzene was obtained from s. d. fine chem. (India) and was used as received.

6.2.2. Synthesis of Organoclays

MMT was purified by sedimentation technique as discussed in literature [17]. The purified clay fractions were obtained by dispersing 150g of bentonite lumps (R-MMT) in 10 L of deionized water (1.5 per cent w/v), and was allowed to swell overnight, stirred (200 rpm) for 30 min. The supernatant slurry having desired clay particles size (< 2 µm) was collected after pre-calculated time (10 h), height (15 cm) at room temperature (27 C) according to the Stoke's law of sedimentation. The slurry obtained (1.02 per cent w/v) was dried and designated as MMT. The cation exchange capacity (CEC) of MMT was measured by standard ammonium acetate method (pH 7.0) and found to be 90 meq/100g of clay.

The organoclays were synthesized by exchanging 90 meq of exchangeable cation per 100 g of MMT using different organic modifiers; 1 per cent solution of hexadecyltrimethylammonium bromide (3.4 g), stearyldimethylbenzylammonium chloride (4.1 g) and dioctadecyl-dimethylammonium chloride (5.4 g) were added within 45 min at 80 C under vigorous stirring to three beakers, each contained 10.2 g of MMT dispersed in 1 L of de-ionized water. Organoclays synthesized were filtered, washed with hot deionized water till free from halide ion (tested by 0.01M $AgNO_3$ solution), dried at 60 C. The dried organoclay was ground and passed through different sieves. Samples obtained were designated as HDTA 90, SDBA 90 and DODA 90. The partially organically modified MMT were synthesized by interacting 10.2g of MMT dispersed in 1 L of de-ionized water with 3.2 (70 meq/100g of MMT) and 2.3 g (50 meq/100g of MMT) of stearyldimethylbenzylammonium chloride in each beaker under the same conditions as described above and designated as SDBA 70 and SDBA 50 respectively.

6.2.3. Batch Experiments

The stock solution of nitrobenzene in water was prepared by dissolving 3.4 g of nitrobenzene in 2 L de-ionized water and stirred for 48 h at room temperature (27 C). Kinetic experiments were conducted to determine the length of time necessary for nitrobenzene solution to reach sorptive equilibrium with different organoclays (HDTA 90, SDBA 90 and DODA 90). The experiments were performed in 50 mL cylinder capped with standard glass cap. For each kinetic experiment, 50 mg of organoclay was placed in 50 mL cylinder containing aqueous nitrobenzene solution (516 mg/L). The cylinders were placed on a rotating shaker at room temperature (27 C). Samples were withdrawn at intervals of 0.08, 0.25, 0.5, 1, 2, 5, 12, 24 h and were analyzed for concentration of nitrobenzene in solution.

The sorption isotherm experiments of nitrobenzene onto HDTA 90, SDBA 90 and DODA 90 were performed in a batch experiment. A known amount of sorbent (50 mg) was placed in a 50 mL cylinder containing aqueous nitrobenzene solution with varying concentrations (50-1500 mg/L). The experiments were performed on shaker for 5 h at room temperature (27 C). After sorption reached equilibrium, the solutions were analyzed for the remaining concentration of nitrobenzene.

6.2.4. Column Experiments

Fixed bed sorption studies were carried out in jacketed 80 mm glass column with an inside diameter of 5 mm. The schematic representation of the experimental set-up is shown in Figure 6.1.

A glass wool was inserted to one end of the column. 1 g of organoclay was then placed into the column to obtain the organoclay bed. A second portion of glass wool was plugged to another end of the column in order

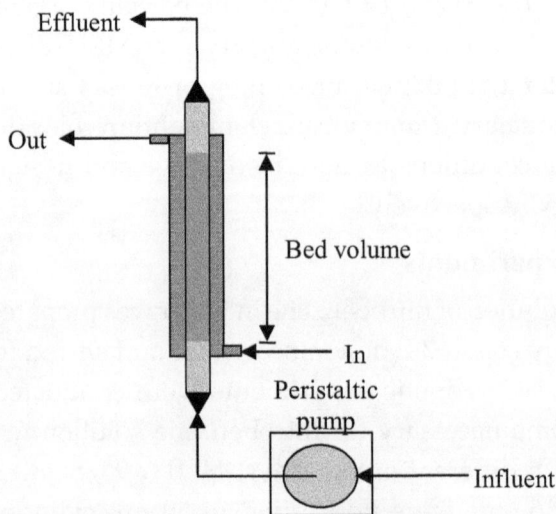

Figure 6.1. Schematic representation of fixed-bed experimental set-up.

to prevent the loss of the organoclays. The aqueous solution of nitrobenzene with a known sorbate concentration was then fed from the bottom of the column to minimize channeling at a desired flow rate controlled by a peristaltic pump (Cole-Parmer, Masterflex – 7518-00) and samples in the effluent from the top of the column were taken at the preset time intervals and were analyzed as described above until the influent concentration of the contaminant equals that of the effluent. In the fixed bed experiments, we have also studied the effect of particle size of sorbent, flow rate, concentration of sorbate, and temperature on breakthrough curves using SDBA 90 organoclay. In addition, we have also studied the effect of partially exchanged MMT with quaternary ammonium cation (SDBA 70 and SDBA 50) on breakthrough curves.

6.2.5. Characterization

Powder X-ray diffraction (PXRD) analysis was carried out with a Phillips powder diffractometer X' Pert MPD using PW3123/00 curved Cu-filtered Cu-Kα (λ=1.54056) radiation with slow scan of 0.3 degree/ second in 2-10 2θ degree for organoclays. Fourier transform infrared spectra (FT-IR) were measured with Perkin-Elmer, GX-FTIR using KBr pellet. The UV-visible absorbance of aqueous solutions of nitrobenzene was measured at λ_{max} = 268 nm using a Cary 500 UV-Visible spectrophotometer (Varian) equipped with a quartz cell having a path length of 1 cm. The concentration of nitrobenzene in the solution was determined using a calibration curve of aqueous nitrobenzene prepared with known concentrations.

6.3. Results and Discussion

6.3.1. XRD and FT-IR of Organoclays

The XRD and FT-IR for organoclays synthesized using different organic modifier and organoclays with different amount of organic modifier are shown in Figure 6.2. The interlayer spacing, d_{001} of DODA 90, SDBA 90, HDTA 90 and MMT is 3.0, 2.6, 1.9 and 1.2 nm, explains the effect of size of alkyl chain length of quaternary ammonium cation situated in MMT and indicates organic modifiers are intercalated into the interlayer space of MMT. Organoclays with different amount of organic modifier, SDBA 70 and SDBA 50 have d_{001} of 1.8 and 1.6 nm. The arrangement of the intercalated surfactant cations depends on the layer charge and alkyl chain

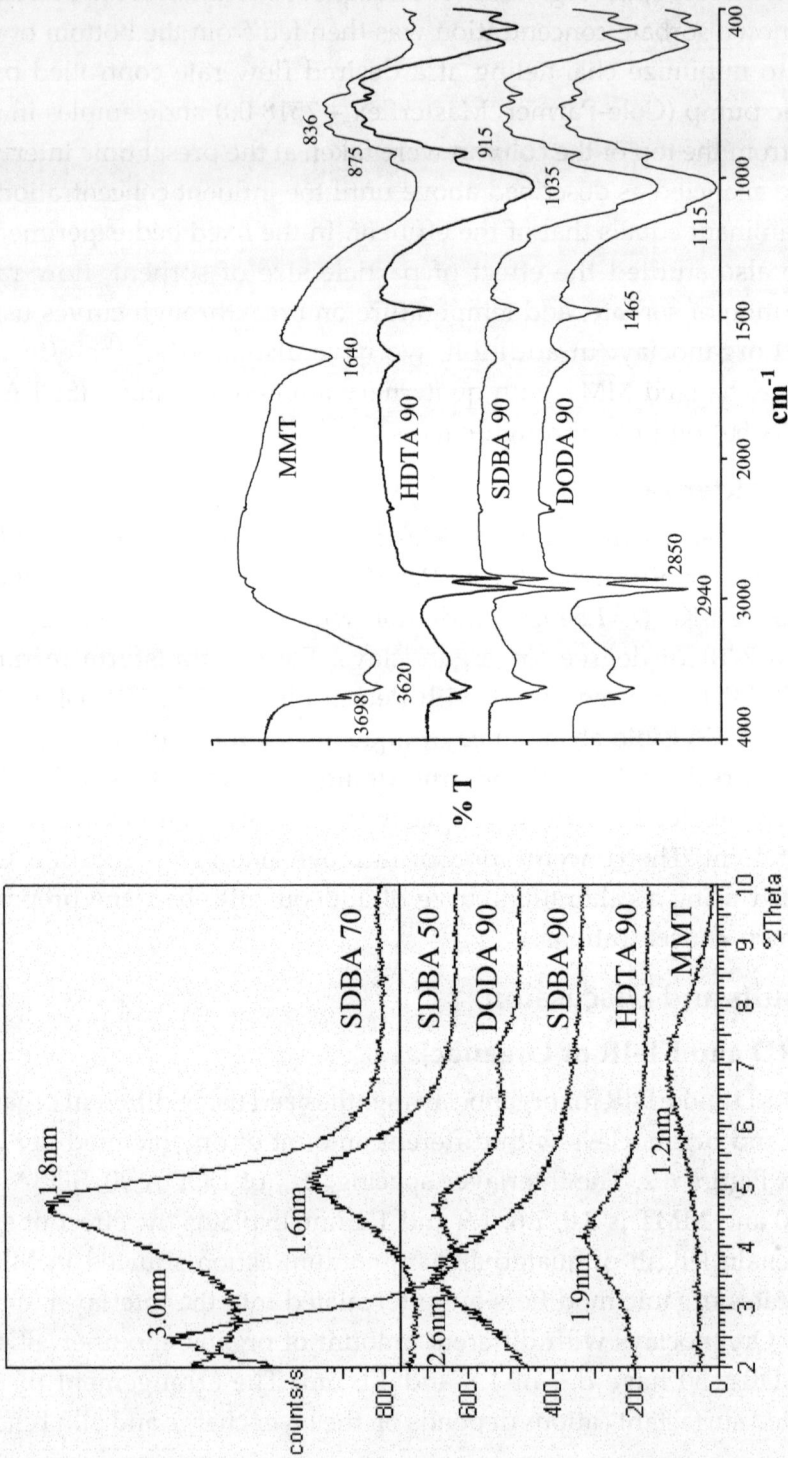

Figure 6.2. XRD pattern and FT-IR spectrum of organoclays.

length. Short chain alkylammonium ions are arranged in monolayers, longer chain alkylammonium ions in bilayers with the alkyl chain axes parallel to the silicate layers. The monolayer has a basal spacing of ~1.4 nm, the bilayer of ~1.8 nm. The monolayer rearranges in to the bilayer when the area of the flat-lying alkylammonium ions becomes larger than the equivalent area. Three layer structures of kinked alkyl chains are observed with highly charged MMT and/or long surfactants cations. This trimolecular arrangement exhibits a basal spacing of ~2.2 nm. Paraffin-type arrangements in the interlayer space of MMT are formed by quaternary alkylammonium ions with two or more long alkyl chains [18-20]. The arrangement of organic modifier in DODA 90 and SDBA 90 is paraffin and trimolecular type, respectively. HDTA 90 has bilayer arrangement of organic modifier in MMT. SDBA 70 and SDBA 50 have bilayer and nearly monolayer arrangement of Stearyldimethyl benzylammonium cation, respectively into interlayer spacing of MMT.

FT-IR spectra of MMT and organoclays (SDBA 90, HDTA 90 and DODA 90) are shown in Figure 6.2. Peaks at 3620 and 3698cm^{-1} are due to -OH band stretch for Al-OH, Mg-OH and Si-OH. The shoulders and broadness of the -OH bands are mainly due to contributions of several structural -OH groups occurring in smectite. The overlaid absorption peaks in the region of 1640cm^{-1} in the FT-IR spectrum is attributed to -OH bending

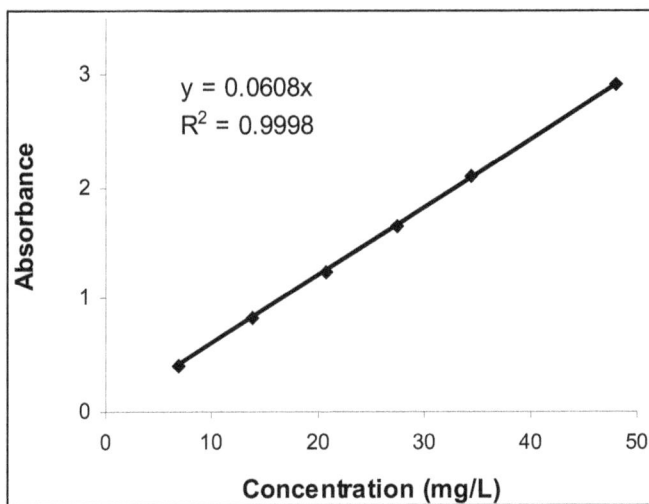

Figure 6.3. Standard plot for the aqueous nitrobenzene of known concentration of nitrobenzene in distilled water.

mode of water (adsorbed water). IR peaks at 915, 875 and 836cm^{-1} are attributed to AlAlOH, AlFeOH and AlMgOH bending vibration respectively. Peaks at 2940 and 2850cm^{-1} for organoclays, are ascribed to the asymmetric and symmetric vibration of methylene groups $(CH_2)_n$ of the aliphatic carbon chain. In addition, there is also HCH stretching vibration band at 1465cm^{-1} in the IR spectrum of all organoclays. FT-IR studies clearly indicate the formation of organic–inorganic hybrids [21-24].

6.3.2. Equilibrium Kinetics

As shown in Figure 6.3, the standard plot for the aqueous nitrobenzene of known concentration of nitrobenzene in distilled water is plotted. This plot have used for the determination of nitrobenzene in unknown solution obtained after sorption of aqueous nitrobenzene on organoclays. The amount of nitrobenzene sorbed with time is given in Figure 3. Initially, sorption of nitrobenzene occurred rapidly up to 1 h and as the time progresses the sorption was increased slowly. The lines shown in Figure 3 are moving average of the experimental results. The solute concentration and amount of sorbent used in this study was 516 mg/L and 50 mg

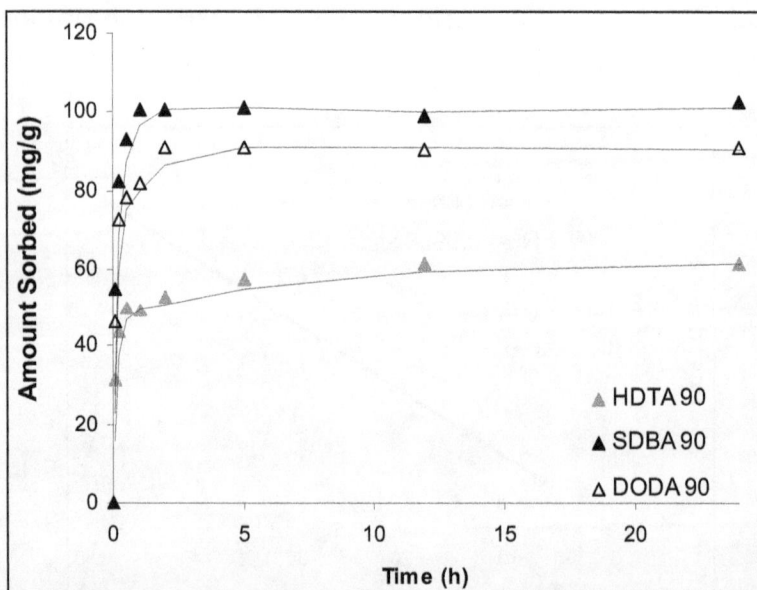

Figure 6.4. Kinetic study of sorption of nitrobenzene on HDTA 90, SDBA 90 and DODA 90 (Sorption conditions: - Sorbent dosage: 50mg/50mL; Sorbate concentration: 516mg/L; Size of sorbent: (-) 100 - (+) 200 mesh size; Temperature: 27C).

respectively. It can be seen from the graph that the plateau took place around at 2 h for SDBA 90 and DADO 90 and it was more than 5 h for HDTA 90. After this, sorption curve was horizontal, indicates saturation was established. The sorption of nitrobenzene over HDTA 90 is lower than SDBA 90 and DADO 90. The time, 5 h, has been taken as equilibrium time.

6.3.3. Sorption Isotherm

The amount of sorbate sorbed per unit weight of sorbent and the equilibrium concentration of sorbate in solution at constant temperature, are usually represented by sorption isotherms, which is of importance in the design of sorption systems. The sorption isotherms of nitrobenzene on HDTA 90, SDBA 90 and DODA 90 at 27C are shown in Figure 6.5. All sorption isotherms are approximately linear over a wide range of equilibrium aqueous concentrations of nitrobenzene (50-1300 mg/L).

Sorption may suggest a partitioning effect, such as in a liquid–liquid extraction process where the organic phase present in the clay galleries acts as a solvent for nitrobenzene molecules. The partitioning effect may

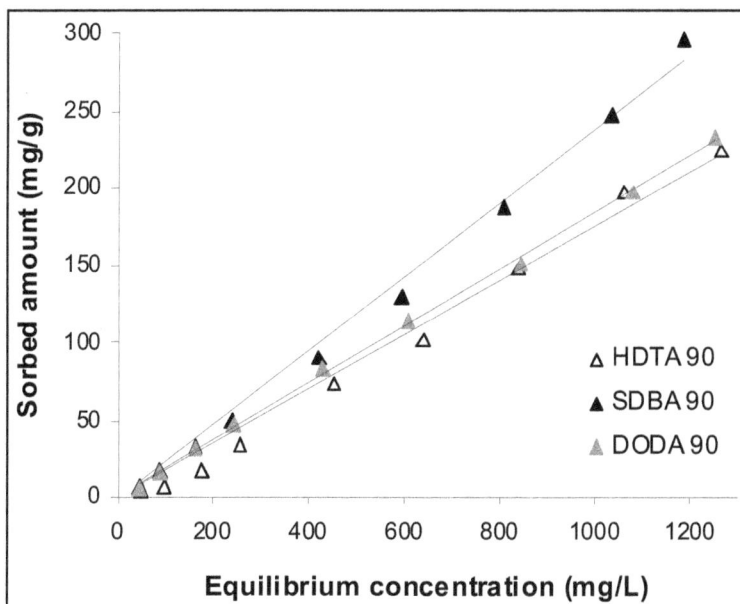

Figure 6.5. Sorption isotherm of nitrobenzene on HDTA 90, SDBA 90 and DODA 90 (Sorption conditions: - Sorbent dosage: 0.05g/50mL; Sorbate concentration: 50-1500mg/L; Size of sorbent: (-) 100 - (+) 200 mesh size; Time for equilibrium: 5hrs; Temperature: 27C).

be attributed to the long alkyl chains of the quaternary ammonium cations and it is favored by the interlayer expansion.

The lines in Figure 6.5 are fitted to show the linear regression. The distribution coefficient for SDBA 90, DODA 90 and HDTA 90 is 0.238, 0.184 and 0.175 L/g, respectively. As the concentration of nitrobenzene increases, the sorption capacity of organoclays also increases linearly. HDTA 90 and DODA 90 isotherms exhibited the almost the same trends, whereas a higher nitrobenzene sorption capacity was observed in the case of SDBA 90. A possible explanation for this enhanced dissolving power is the increased chemical affinity between the benzyl group of the quaternary ammonium cations and nitrobenzene. From the sorption isotherm, sorption capacity for organoclays are in the order of SDBA 90 > DODA 90 > HDTA 90. Thus, SDBA 90 has been used for the fixed-bed experiments.

6.3.4. Fixed-Bed Experiments

In the dynamic sorption studies, the sorbent (organoclay) was loaded in column with dimension of 50mm length and 5mm diameter, through which the aqueous solution of the nitrobenzene is passed. During its passage through the bed, the solution continuously meets a fresh part of the sorbent and tends to establish equilibrium. However, as the time of contact with a given part of the sorbent is limited, a true equilibrium is never attained [25-26]. As the solution passes continuously through the bed, the sorption zone moves upwards and when the sorption zone reaches the top of the bed the sorbate starts coming in the outlet stream, the system said to reach breakthrough point. The solute concentration in the effluent rises rapidly as the sorption zone passes through the top of the bed until it eventually reaches the initial concentration ($C/Co = 1.0$). In the latter stages (C/Co e" 0.9), a little sorption takes place since the bed is practically in equilibrium with the feed solution. The shape and time of appearance of the breakthrough curve greatly influence the method of operating a fixed-bed sorbent. The curves generally have an S-shape but they may be steep or relatively flat and in some cases considerably distorted. The U.S. Environmental Protection Agency (EPA) recommends that levels in lakes and streams should be limited to 17 parts of nitrobenzene per million parts of water (17 ppm) to prevent possible health effects from drinking water or eating fish contaminated with nitrobenzene. Thus, in the present study, Breakthrough point is considered at 17 mg/L effluent concentration and the exhaust time were taken at $C/C_0 = 0.9$.

The breakthrough curves expressed in terms of C/Co and time for sorption of aqueous nitrobenzene on organoclays are shown in Figure 6.6-6.10. From the breakthrough curves, important column parameters such as time for primary sorption zone to move up its length (t_z), total time involved for establishment of primary sorption zone (t_E), rate at which the exchange zone is moving up through the bed (U_z), fractional capacity (F), the height of the exchange zone (h_z) and percentage of the total column saturated at breakthrough (per cent S) are calculated on the basis of equations 1-7 [27-29].

The time required for the exchange zone to move the length of its own height up/down the column once it has become established is;

$$t_z = \frac{V_E - V_B}{Q_W} \tag{1}$$

where,

V_E: Total volume of wastewater treated to the point of exhaustion (1);

V_B: Total volume of wastewater treated to the point of breakthrough (1);

Q_w: Wastewater flow rate (1/h).

The time required for the exchange zone to become established and move completely out of the bed is;

$$t_E = \frac{V_E}{Q_W} \tag{2}$$

Rate at which the exchange zone is moving up or down through the bed is

$$U_Z = \frac{h_Z}{t_z} = -\frac{h}{t_E - t_f} \tag{3}$$

where,

h_z: Height of exchange zone (cm)

h: Total bed depth (cm)

t_f: Time required for the exchange zone to initially form (h)

Rearranging Eq. (3) provides an expression for the height of the exchange zone as given below,

$$h_z = \frac{h(h_Z)}{t_E - t_f} \tag{4}$$

The value of t_f can be calculated as follows;

$$t_f = (1 - F)t_Z \tag{5}$$

At breakthrough the fraction of adsorbate present in the adsorption zone still possessing ability to remove solute is;

$$F = \frac{S_Z}{S_{max}} = \frac{\int_{V_B}^{V_E}(C_0 - C)dV}{C_0(V_E - V_B)} \tag{6}$$

where,

C_0: Initial solute concentration (mg/l);

S_z: Amount of solute that has been removed by the adsorption zone from breakthrough to exhaustion

S_{max}: Amount of solute removed by the adsorption zone if completely exhausted

The percentage of the total column saturated at breakthrough is

$$Per cent saturation = \frac{h + (F-1)h_Z}{h} \times 100 \tag{7}$$

The breakthrough capacity indicates the sorption capacity of organoclay to the breakthrough point and was measured by $V_B \times C_0/W$, Where W is the weight of the sorbent.

6.3.4.1. Effect of Feed Rate

The measured breakthrough curves of nitrobenzene (461 mg/L) on the SDBA 90 (1 g) bed at different flow rates are shown in Figure 6.6. The breakthrough point (C/Co at effluent concentration of 17 mg/L) occurs faster with increase the flow rate. The important column behavior parameters are shown in Table 6.1. The t_Z and t_E is 408 and 583min (0.6 mL/min); 295 and 370min (1.0 mL/min); 193 and 233 (1.5 mL/min), respectively. In the case of SDBA 90 with particle size of (-)60 – (+) 100, the fractional capacity (F) of the column in the sorption zone from

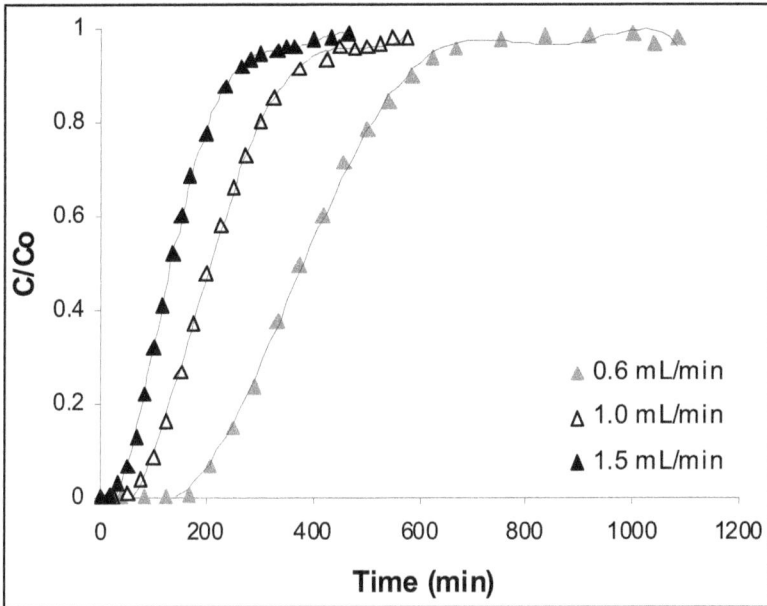

Figure 6.6. Effect of flow rate of sorbate solution on breakthrough curve of sorption of nitrobenzene on SDBA 90 (Sorption conditions: - Sorbent: 1g; Bed length: 50mm; Bed diameter: 5mm; Sorbate concentration: 461mg/L; Temperature: 27C; Size of sorbent: (-)60 - (+)100 mesh size).

breakthrough point to continue to remove solute from solution is 0.92, 0.92 and 0.85 and the percent saturation at breakpoint is 93.7, 93.1 and 85.4 per cent for the feed rate of 0.6, 1.0 and 1.5 mL/min, respectively.

The rate of exchange zone is increases with increase in the feed rate. The breakthrough capacity of nitrobenzene sorption on SDBA 90 decreases with increase in the flow rate. This is due to fact that as the feed rate increases the sorbate gets lower contact time to diffuse into the sorbent particles. The column capacity was found to be higher than batch capacity as calculated by sorption isotherms. A higher capacity of column operations was established by a continuously large concentration gradient at the interface zone as it passed through the column, while the concentration gradient decreased with time in a batch isotherm test.

6.3.4.2. Effect of Feed Concentration

The effect of feed concentration is illustrated in Figure 6.7. Breakthrough point appears faster with increasing feed concentration. For feed concentration of 252 and 763 mg/L, the values of t_z, t_E, F and per

Table 6.1. Important column behavior parameters.

Sorbent	SDBA 90	SDBA 90		SDBA 90	SDBA 90	SDBA 90	SDBA 50	SDBA 70	SDBA 90
Feed rate (mL/min)	**0.6**	**1.0**	**1.5**	1.0	1.0	1.0	1.0	0.6	1.0
Feed concentration (mg/L)	461	461		461	**252**	**763**	461	461	461
Sorbent size (ASTM mesh size)	(-)60 - (+)100	(-)60 - (+)100		**(-)30 - (+)60**	(-)60 - (+)100	(-)60 - (+)100	(-)60 - (+)100		(-)60 - (+)100
Temperature (C)	27	27		27	27	27	27	27	**17**
V_B (mL)	105	75	60	30	110	60	54	75	80
V_E (mL)	350	370	350	450	420	550	276	399	450
t_z (min)	408	295	193	420	310	490	370	540	370
t_E (min)	583	370	233	450	420	550	460	665	450
F	0.92	0.92	0.85	0.88	0.82	0.8	0.79	0.9	0.87
h_z (cm)	3.7	4.3	4.8	5.3	4.3	5.4	4.8	4.4	4.6
U_z (cm/h)	0.55	0.87	1.47	0.75	0.82	0.66	0.79	0.49	0.74
per cent S	93.7	93.1	85.4	87.2	84.5	78.9	79.1	91.5	88.4
Breakthrough capacity (mg/g)	48.4	34.6	27.7	13.8	27.7	44.8	24.9	34.6	36.9

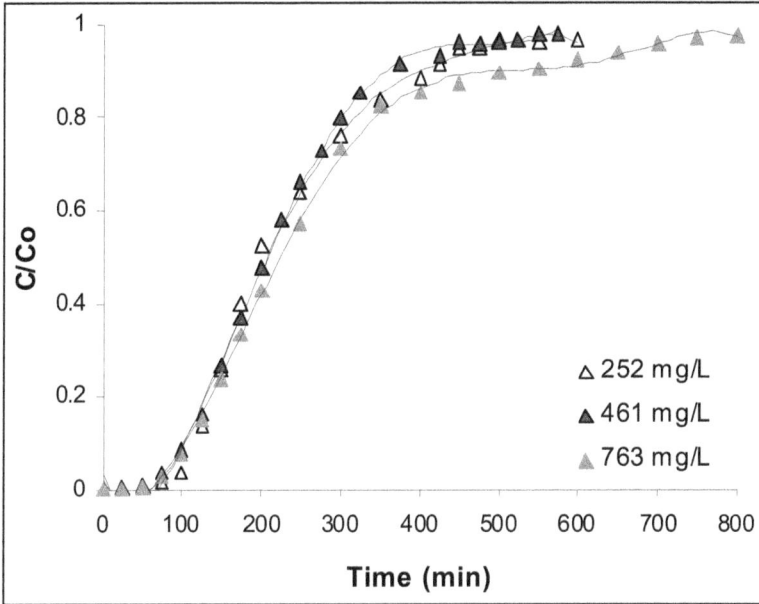

Figure 6.7. Effect of concentration of sorbate solution on breakthrough curve of sorption of nitrobenzene on SDBA 90 (Sorption conditions: - Sorbent: 1 g; Bed length: 50 mm; Bed diameter: 5 mm; Flow rate: 1 mL/min; Temperature: 27 C; Size of sorbent: (-) 60 - (+) 100 mesh size).

cent S are 310 and 490 min, 420 and 550 min, 0.82 and 8, 84.5 and 78.9 per cent, respectively as shown in Table 6.1. The rate of exchange zone (Uz) decreases when increases the feed concentration. The breakthrough capacity is also increases with increase in feed concentration since the equilibrium sorption isotherm is linear. The breakthrough capacity for feed concentration of 252 mg/L is around 50 per cent of its equilibrium sorption capacity and for 461 and 763 mg/L, it is 30 and 25 per cent of its equilibrium sorption capacity.

6.3.4.3. Effect of Size of Sorbent

The size of the sorbent plays an important role in fixed-bed system as shown in Figure 6.8. SDBA 90 with (-)30 - (+)60 and (-)60 - (+)100 mesh size were used in this study for column sorption. The breakthrough point of nitrobenzene occurs slowly in SDBA 90 with fine particle size compare to coarser particle size.

This is because the faster diffusion of nitrobenzene in SDBA 90 with fine particles and thus, it can have a high breakthrough capacity (34.6

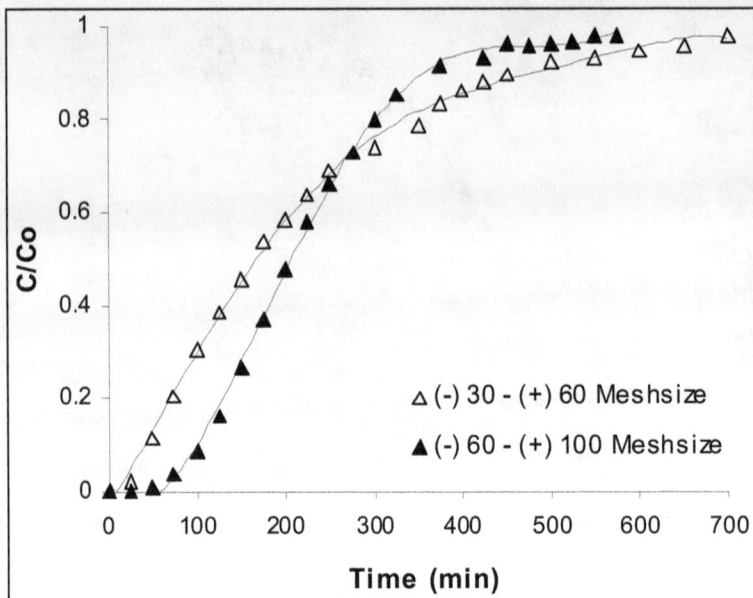

Figure 6.8. Effect of particle size of SDBA 90 on breakthrough curve of sorption of nitrobenzene (Sorption conditions: - Sorbent: 1g; Bed length: 50mm (60-100 mesh), 53 mm (30-60); Bed diameter: 5mm; Sorbate concentration: 461mg/L; Temperature: 27C; Flow rate: 1mL/min).

mg/g) compare to coarser particles of SDBA 90 which is having breakthrough capacity of 13.8 mg/g. The t_Z, t_E, F and per cent S is 420 min, 450 min, 0.88 and 87.2 per cent. The rate of exchange zone is 0.8cm/ h. This explains that the percent saturation is higher in lower as compare to coarser particle size. The height of exchange zone (h_Z) is also higher (5.3 cm) while the sorption study carried out using (-)30 - (+)60 mesh sized particles. The h_Z for (-)60 - (+)100 mesh sized particles is 4.3 cm. The rate of exchange zone is decreases with decrease in size of the SDBA 90.

6.3.4.4. Effect of Amount of Organic Moiety Exchanged in MMT

The organic modification of MMT substantially increases the sorption capacity of nonpolar organic contaminants from wastewater. To illustrate this effect, organoclay with different amount of organic moiety (SDBA 70 and SDBA 50) were synthesized and employed for the sorption of aqueous nitrobenzene in fixed-bed system as shown in Figure 6.9. The breakthrough point of nitrobenzene appears faster on sorbent with lower organic modifier. The t_Z and t_E is 470 and 460 min (SDBA 50); 540 and 665 min

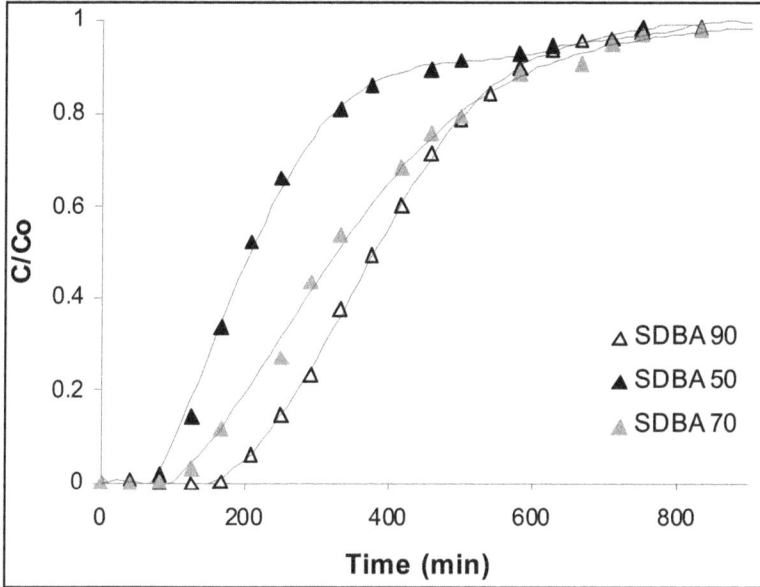

Figure 6.9. Effect of amount of organic moiety exchanged with MMT on breakthrough curve of sorption of nitrobenzene on SDBA 90 (Sorption conditions: - Sorbent: 1g; Bed length: 50 mm (SDBA 90), 43 mm (SDBA 70), 40 mm (SDBA 50); Bed diameter: 5mm; Flow rate: 1.0mL/min; Sorbate concentration: 461mg/L; Temperature: 27C; Size of sorbent: (-) 60 - (+) 100 mesh size).

(SDBA 70), respectively. The fractional capacity (F) and per cent S decreases while h_z and U_z increases with decrease in amount of organic modifier in sorbent. The per cent S for SDBA 70 and SDBA 50 is 91.5 and 79.1, respectively. The breakthrough capacity was also decreases with decrease in the amount of organic moiety in organoclay, in the order of 44.6 mg/g for SDBA 90, 34.6 mg/g for SDBA 70 and 24.9 mg/g for SDBA 50.

6.3.4.5. Effect of Temperature and Desorption

The temperature of the sorption medium is also an important parameter for designing a fixed-bed sorption setup. The temperature effect on breakthrough curve was studied at 27 C (room temperature) and 17 C. We were also tried to get data from higher temperature (37 C), but failed, due to swelling as well as breaking of organoclay particles at higher temperature which blocked the column and substantially reduced the effluent flow rate. The t_z and t_E is 370 and 450 min. at 17C. The saturation at breakthrough point and fractional capacity are 88.4 per cent and 0.87,

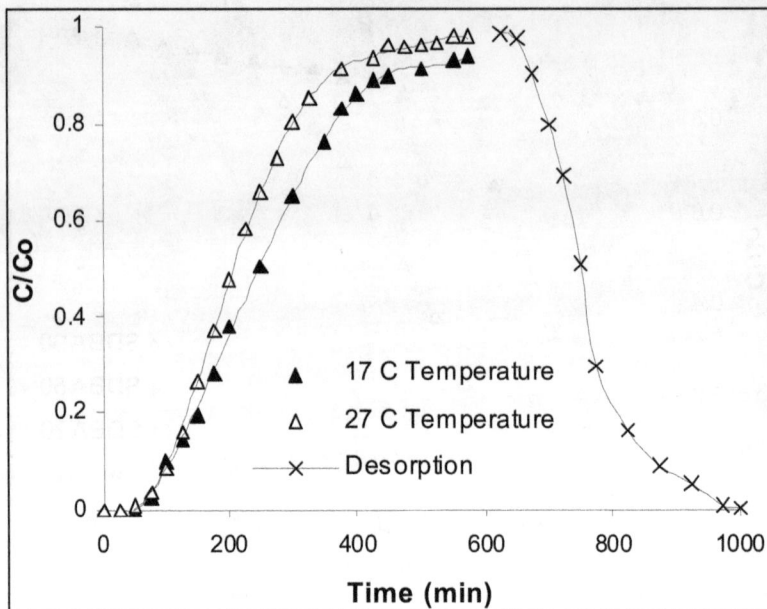

Figure 6.10. Effect of temperature on breakthrough curve of sorption of nitrobenzene on SDBA 90 (Sorption conditions: - Sorbent: 1g; Bed length: 50mm; Bed diameter: 5mm; Flow rate: 1.0 mL/min; Sorbate concentration: 461mg/L; Size of sorbent: (-) 60 - (+) 100 mesh size) and desorption using water at 27C temperature.

respectively which are lower than dynamic sorption measurement carried out at room temperature. The height of exchange zone is 4.6 cm is higher than the dynamic sorption at room temperature. These parameters show that at 17 C, even though the equilibrium breakthrough capacity is higher the diffusion of nitrobenzene is slower than that at room temperature sorption which can be seen as the broader breakthrough curve given in Figure 6.10.

The organoclay column is generally dumped as solid waste after sorption of organic contaminants from wastewater. As stated earlier, the phenomenon involved in sorption of nitrobenzene over organoclay is partitioning. Elution of sorbate with simultaneous chemical regeneration by suitable solvent has been tried by passing water through the column.

Desorption of nitrobenzene were carried out in-situ at room temperature after sorption of aqueous nitrobenzene at 17 C temperature as shown in Figure 6.10. 375 mL of water is sufficient for the almost complete desorption of nitrobenzene, at the water floe rate of 1 mL/min.

It is clear that a cyclic process for the recovery of nitrobenzene is feasible by using two or more sorbent column in parallel, in which one column is in the sorption cycle while other will be in regeneration cycle.

References

1. Upson R. T. and Burns S. E., *J. Collo. Inter. Sci.*, 297, 70, 2006.

2. Chatterjee A., Ebina T., Iwasaki T. and Mizukami F., *J. Chem. Phys.*, 118(22), 10212, 2003.

3. Agency for Toxic Substances and Disease Registry (ATSDR), Toxicological Profile for Nitrobenzene; Public Health Service, *U.S. Department of Health and Human Services*, Atlanta, GA, available at http://www.atsdr.cdc.gov/taxfaq.html.

4. Haigler B. E. and Spain J. C., *Appl. Environ. Microbiol.*, 57(11), 3156, 1991.

5. Qin Q., Ma J. and Liu K., *J. Collo. Inter. Sci.*, 315, 80, 2005.

6. Patel H. A., Somani R. S., Bajaj H. C. and Jasra R. V., *Bull. Mater. Sci.*, 29, 133, 2006.

7. Alther G., *Waste Manag.*, 22, 507, 2002.

8. Tayade R. J., Kulkarni R. G. and Jasra R. V., *Ind. Eng. Chem. Res.*, 45, 922, 2006.

9. Redding A. Z., Burns S. E., Upson R. T. and Anderson E. F., *J. Collo. Inter. Sci.*, 250, 261, 2002.

10. Beall, G. W., *Appl. Clay Sci.*, 24, 11, 2003.

11. Bergaya, F. Theng B. K. G. and Lagaly G., Handbook of clay science, First Edition, *Elsevier Scientific Publication*, The Netherlands, 2006.

12. Boyd S. A., Sheng G., Teppen B. J. and Johnston C. T., *Environ. Sci. Technol.*, 35, 4227, 2001.

13. Zhu L., Gren X. and Yu S., *Environ. Sci. Technol.*, 32, 3374, 1998.

14. Zhu L., Li Y. and Zhang J., *Environ. Sci. Technol.*, 31, 1407, 1997.

15. Farkas A. and Dekany I., *Collo. Polym. Sci.*, 279, 459, 2001.

16. Pernyeszi T., Kasteel R., Witthuhn B., Klahre P., Vereecken H. and Klumpp E., *Appl. Clay Sci.*, 32, 179, 2006.

17. Patel H. A., Somani R. S., Bajaj H. C. and Jasra R. V., *Curr. Sci.*, 92(2), 1, 2006.

18. Paul D. R., Zeng Q. H., Yu A. B. and Lu, G. Q., *J. Collo. Inter. Sci.*, 292, 462, 2005.

19. Patel H. A., Somani R. S., Bajaj H. C. and Jasra, R. V., *Curr. Sci.*, 92(7), 1004, 2007.

20. Vaia R. A., Teukolsky R. K. and Giannelis E. P., *Chem. Mater.*, 6, 1017, 1994.

21. Lee J.Y. and Lee H. K., *Mater. Chem. Phys.*, 85, 410, 2004.

22. Madejova J., *Vibrat. Spectro.*, 31, 1, 2003.

23. Tyagi B., Chudasama C. D. and Jasra R.V., *Spectroch. Acta Part A*, 64 (2), 273, 2006.

24. Xi Y., Ding Z., Hongping H. and Frosr R. L., *Spectro. Acta Part A*, 61, 515, 2005.

25. Goyal M., Singh S. and Bansal R. C., *Carbon Sci.*, 5(4), 170, 2004.

26. Attia A. A., Girgis B. S. and Fathy N. A., *Dyes and Pigments*, 76, 282, 2008.

27. Gupta V. K., Mohan D., Suhas and Singh K. P., *Ind. Eng. Chem. Res.*, 45, 1113, 2006.

28. Gupta V. K., Srivastava S. K. and Mohan D., *Ind. Eng. Chem. Res.*, 36, 2207, 1997.

29. Adak A., Bandyopadhyay M. and Pal A., *Dyes and Pigments*, 69, 245, 2006.

Chapter 7
Summary, Conclusions and Future Scopes

7.1. Summary and Conclusions

The present thesis describes the beneficiation of Indian bentonites by sedimentation and chemical treatments. The purified bentonite (montmorillonite) is used for the synthesis of nanoclays using various quaternary ammonium and phosphonium salts by ion exchange reaction. The synthesized nanoclays are employed as reinforcement for polymer nanocomposites and solvents which are used for paints, supporting materials for metal nanoparticles and adsorption of aqueous nitrobenzene. The physico-chemical properties of nanoclays, polymer nanocomposites and metal nanoparticles anchored nanoclays are characterized by powder X-ray diffraction, FT-IR spectroscopy, thermogravimetric analysis, particle size distribution, elemental analysis by CHN analyzer and ICP-AES and transmission electron microscopy.

The **Chapter 1** comprises introduction of nanoclays and its applications in various fields. The classification, purification and structural properties of clay minerals are discussed. The synthesis methodology for nanoclays and characterization techniques used for nanoclays are illustrated. The improvements in mechanical and thermal properties of polymer nanocomposites by addition of few weight percent of nanoclay in polymer are also discussed. The arrangement of organic modifier within the interlayer space of montmorillonite with respect to size and concentration of organic modifier are given. The applications of nanoclays for polymer nanocomposites, rheological modifier for paints, inks and greases, and nanoclays for wastewater treatment are reviewed.

The **Chapter 2** discusses the sedimentation technique based on Stoke's Law of sedimentation is simple and cost effective method for the purification of bentonites. The beneficiation study of two major bentonite deposits (Gujarat and Rajasthan) of India are carried out and concluded that these beneficiated bentonite can be used for the synthesis of nanoclays. The chemical treatment using both organic and inorganic acids improve the brightness of the clay but at the same time it is reduced CEC and swelling volume which are very important propertied for the synthesis of nanoclays. The sodium dithionite treatment is only removed non-structural iron from the bentonite while structural iron (Nontronite) reduced during treatment and re-oxidized after treatment.

In the **Chapter 3**, the synthesis and characterization of nanoclays using purified MMT and quaternary ammonium/phosphonium salts are discussed. The hydrophobicity, basal spacing and particle size of nanoclays directly depends on the chain length of organic modifiers as well as percentage of organic modifier exchanged to MMT. The particle size of nanoclays is observed to depend on the reaction temperature. The finer particles are obtained by synthesizing nanoclays at higher temperature as compared to that prepared at lower temperature. The arrangement of organic modifier such as monolayer, bilayer and paraffin type in the interlayer space of the MMT depends on the alkyl chain length of organic modifier. The highest thermal stability of the ammonium based nanoclays observed for nanoclay modified with organic modifier with aromatic and long alkyl chain. The finer particle size distribution was observed for the intercalated MMT with longer chain phosphonium ions because the alkyl chains prevented silicate platelets from aggregation. The phenyl group substituted phosphonium MMT showed the highest thermal stability of 350–400 °C (5 per cent decomposition). Tetrabutylphosphonium MMT was stable as tetraphenylphosphonium MMT due to the high thermal stability of the tetrabutylphosphonium cation.

Compounding of nanoclays with PP is discussed in **Chapter 4**. Nanoclays synthesized from Indian bentonite for PCN application have identical properties except basal spacing. A small addition of nanoclays in PP drastically improved mechanical properties. PCNs with nanoclay (PCN 2) synthesized from Indian bentonite shows almost similar properties to PCNs with imported nanoclay (PCN 1). WAXD studies demonstrated intercalation of PP in nanoclay rather than exfoliation. The tensile modulus increased by 41 and 39 per cent for PCN 1 and PCN 2 with respect to PP. The flexural modulus for PCN 1 and PCN 2 is also increases by 23 and 22 per cent by incorporation of 5 per cent nanoclay in PP along with 5 per cent MA-g-PP. The impact strength of the PCNs decreases by incorporation of nanoclays. Organoclays can be also used for rheological modifier for paint formulations. The exfoliation of organoclay depends on the polarity of solvent and organic modifier used for the synthesis of organoclays. The weak or moderate hydrogen bonding group within solvent resulted into lower gel volume. The organic modifier with two long alkyl chain (OC 3) showed highest gel volume in toluene.

The **Chapter 5** demonstrates the novel synthetic route for synthesis of Pd and Rh metal nanoparticles supported on MMT and POMM is resulted metallic nanoparticles. PXRD pattern confirms the formation of Pd and Rh metal nanoparticles in MMT and POMM. Agglomeration of Pd and Rh metal nanoparticles is observed in MMT while the partial organic modification of MMT is controlled the particle size of Pd and Rh with very good dispersion through out POMM. Au and Ag nanoparticles anchored organoclays are synthesized in a single step. The effect of surfactant and reduction path substantially affects the size of the generated Au or Ag nanoparticles. Nearly monodispersed Au nanoparticles are observed while the reduction of gold salt was carried out after the intercalation of organic modifier, *i.e.*, within organoclay. The particle size of Ag nanoparticles is higher than that of Au due to precipitation of AgCl or AgBr during the synthesis which leads to agglomeration of Ag nanoclusters. The HRTEM and PXRD studies prove the formation of Au and Ag nanoparticles anchored organoclays.

Sorption of aqueous nitrobenzene on organoclays in batch and fixed-bed system is discussed in **Chapter 6**. Sorption of nitrobenzene in dynamic condition is technologically important study for wastewater treatment.

The phenomenon involved in sorption of nitrobenzene over organoclay is partition rather than adsorption. Presence of benzyl functionalities in organoclay can increase the sorption capacity of aromatic organic contaminants. The sorption capacity of organoclay is in the order of SDBA 90 > DODA 90 > HDTA 90. The breakthrough capacity is increases when the dynamic sorption carried out using finer particles of SDBA 90 and slower feed rate (0.6 mL/min.) at 27C. The broader breakthrough curves are obtained for higher particle size of SDBA 90, and sorption performed at 17 C. The important column parameters which are useful for designing a column, have evaluated for the sorption of nitrobenzene on organoclay from breakthrough curves. Desorption of nitrobenzene from organoclay is also possible. The present work provided a simple and easy-to-follow method for analyzing the breakthrough characteristics for the sorption of nitrobenzene on the organoclays.

7.2. Future Scopes

As the applications of nanoclays have broadened since few years and the imported cost of the nanoclays is very high, it is necessary to produce nanoclays from the Indian bentonites. Some of the key points which are observed during this study and are significant for future directions are;

☆ It will be possible to further improve the brightness of the Indian bentonites by employing combination of chemical treatments and purification of bentonite by hydrocyclone technique.

☆ The thermal stability of the nanoclay is an important property when it can be applied for engineering plastic and high temperature resistant greases. The thermal stability of nanoclay can be improved by preparing nanoclays using alkyl/aryl imidazolium salts or quaternary ammonium/phosphonium salts with aromatic functionalities.

☆ The complete exfoliation of nanoclays in PP matrix is a key feature of discussion, as up to now there is no report showing complete exfoliation of nanoclay in PP matrix rather than partly intercalated and exfoliated. The exfoliation of nanoclays may be achieved by modification of MMT surface by dual organic modifiers or modifying the PP. We have carried out some of the experiments to study the stability of nanoclays in solvents which are used for paints, however, the applications of nanoclays in paints, inks and cosmetics requires more fundamental study.

☆ Metal nanoparticles supported on MMT are an emerging field. The particle size and stability of nanoparticles can be controlled by nanoclays which are acts as nano-phase reactor. Apart from Pd, Rh, Au and Ag metal nanoparticles, there will be possibilities for synthesizing other valuable metal, metal oxide or bimetallic nanoparticles within the nanoclays for catalytic applications in various organic transformations.

☆ Though the sorption of organic contaminants from wastewater on organoclays have been started quite long back, there is tremendous potential for organoclays to clean the environments and can be technologically important method. There are very limited industries supplying kits of organoclays for wastewater treatment. There is need to emphasizes on the engineering parameters for the sorption system based on organoclays.

www.ingramcontent.com/pod-product-compliance
Lightning Source LLC
Chambersburg PA
CBHW020218290326
41948CB00001B/96